Fisher Blue

A collection of North-east tales and poems

by PETER BUCHAN

Peter Buchan
10/11/88

ISBN 0 9513947 0 3

There is a time to weep,
and a time to laugh.
ECCLESIASTES 3, v.4.

Printed in Great Britain
by W. M. Bett Ltd, Tillicoultry

Contents

List of Plates

Foreword

A new book by Peter Buchan is like a great public event or going on holiday and aabody lookin' forward to it and hopin' for fine weather. Judging by the phenomenal sales of his former books, *Mount Pleasant* and *Fit Like, Skipper?* there is much to look forward to, and no chance of the boatie gaan ashore on the Skerry Rock like the *Mary Jane* in Fisher Blue, one of four poems in the book, the one which supplies the title. But this book is not all fish-heids and herrin' guts, for Peter has gone out into the countryside for some of his stories, and thus farming folk can share in his humorous and varied adventures.

The first time I met Peter at his ain fireside, his book of poems *Mount Pleasant* had been published six times, and yet he had never seriously tried his hand at prose. The next time I met him was on the sunny banks of the river Ugie at Mount Pleasant, where he had gone on a nostalgic walk evoking scenes of his childhood while recuperating from a serious operation. It was the sort of summer afternoon that reflected every precious line he wrote in that title poem which always moistens my eyes when I read it:

> And oh!, the joy on golden days
>   When summer reigned in robes of green,
> To see, a-shimmer in the haze,
>   The lovely scene.
>
> The child is gone, who watched so well
>   The fleeting seasons come and go.
> His shadow cannot catch the spell
>   Of long ago.

But the poet was so much changed after his ordeal, and the light gone out of his eyes, that I failed to recognise him. Then something stirred inside of me and I looked at him and said:

'Man, ye're affa like Peter Buchan, the poet!'

His wife Agnes was close by his side, and she promptly told me: 'But he is Peter Buchan, the poet!'

It made my day.

Recovery was a renaissance for Peter Oxo, as he is fondly known, a period of rejuvenescence, and he has had a dab at the prose with which we are all now familiar. He is the fisherman wordsmith with the magic hammer that beats on the literary anvil like the human heart. His prose pulsates with life; lively, sensitive, penetrating, quirky, funny and real; and his poetry touches the fibre of life, hair, nail and shinbone; nothing escapes his insight into human existence, or his eye for natural beauty in body or in flower, and his word music throbs with feeling.

To construct a story, Peter doesn't have to kill somebody or have them die for dramatic effect. A penchant for blood is not one of his sins, and he can spin a yarn from the most flimsy material, like fishermen having their ears pierced and wearing ear-rings to improve their eyesight, or working in welly boots, which is supposed to diminish it. In the country, it wasn't the welly boots we blamed for failing eyesight, but the hay we stuffed into them to keep them dry.

Peter's deployment of the Buchan Doric is now legendary. He uses it as it has never been used before, and his spelling of the words defies all dictionary convention, but rings true in speech: words like plook (pimple), seerip, worsit, faa clyte (fall hard), joog, foosty (stale), wyte, maik (halfpenny), vricht (joiner), feeties, snoot, rummle, bourachie (small crowd), nae mowse (uncanny), pirn threed, caff-saick, and many, many more. Some of the stories in this new book will gar ye claa far it's nae yokie!

Over the years Peter has been answering the doorbell to a lot o' folk claiming to be the victim or subjects of individual character sketches he had written. At the last count he had half-a-dozen Dunderheids claiming identity, which indicates his perspicacious awareness of human frailty and idiosyncratic behaviour. Long may his doorbell ring for those gentle interlopers who are really the worshippers at his poetic and story-telling shrine.

July 26th, 1988   DAVID TOULMIN

Fisher Blue

Jock an' Daavit bocht a shippie;
    Changed her name to *Mary Jane*.
Spent a heap o' hard-won siller
    Jist to rig her oot again.

Jimmy Anderson, the tinsmith
    Sowdered ilkie broken licht;
Keithie Hutton shued the mizzen,
    Sidney put the compass richt.
Alan Cardno, supervisor
    Wi' the firm o' Milne and Robb,
Trotted up an' doon the jetty
    Like a scout on bob-a-job.
Souter Davidson did the paintin',
    Ilkie deck-board fisher blue;
Geordie Cruickshank did the caulkin',
    Sweirin' he could see richt through.
Kysie sorted up the caipsan,
    Sticker lined the plummer-block.
Geordie Grant cleaned oot the biler,
    Saat an' scale as hard as rock!

'Noo!', says Daavit. 'I'll be skipper!
    I'm the man wi' aa the thocht!'
'Fine!', says Jock. 'Then I'll be driver
    On this gallant ship we've bocht!'
Sic a fancy celebration
    Fin the trial trip wis made!
Bobby Taitie sent a hurley,
    Load wi' pies an' lemonade.

Fourteen weeks athoot a docket
    Onward sailed the *Mary Jane*. . . .
Daavit took the herrin' fivver,
    Jock jist swore, an' swore again.
'Daavit, man! Ye're waar than eeseless!
    Can ye nae dee naething richt?

Ither folk can mak' a livin',
    Yet in debt we're oot o' sicht!
Ticket nivver made a skipper!
    Sookin' bairn could furl a wheel!
Pit her in amon' the herrin'
    Daavit, or we'll aa ging feel!'

'Richt!', says Daavit. 'You that's clivver,
    Come an' tak a spell up here!
Brains I dinna hae for skipper?
    Weel! I'll dee for engineer!
Ficherin' wi' a five-eight spanner,
    Dichtin' wi' a greasy cloot;
Ony feel could fire a biler,
    Shovel't on an' rake it oot!
Sweat-rag nivver made a driver!
    Skill ye need to save the coal!
So, my lad, we'll jist change places,
    I've heen mair than I can thole!'

See her swingin' roon' the jetty,
    Ilkie deck-board fisher blue;
Jock aye tittin' at the fussle,
    Tootin' like a tooteroo!
Daavit peepin' thro' the skylicht;
    Aa the weemin folk wis doon,
Bonny dressed, to see oor heroes
    Settin' oot for Yarmouth toon!

Fylie aifter, Daavit's skirlin',
    'Canna see a thing for steam!
Biler's burstit! Launch the smaa-boat!
    Jock! Ye ken I canna sweem!'

Thro' the clouds o' steam an' sorra
    Comes the sad reply fae Jock,
'Daavit! Nivver mine the smaa-boat!
    Jump! We're on the Skerry Rock!'

The Three Musketeers

For thirty-six hours, the *Meadowsweet* had lain at the head of the loch while the storm raged among the hills. The surface water of the anchorage seemed to be covered in smoke, as the spray was torn up by the wind and driven, in horizontal sheets, towards the entrance, but there was no swell at all. So, with her great mizzen set, the shippie lay at peace, head to wind. Long periods of snow had clothed the hills in a deep, white mantle, right to the water's edge. Now and again, a few deer had been sighted but, apart from these, there was no sign of life, although a straggle of low cottages along the shore betrayed the presence of Man.

There was very little for the crew to do, apart from keeping anchor watch. There was no radio on board and, since fresh reading material was in short supply, the boys either slept, or sat on the 'fiddley', that cosy space between the wheelhouse and the funnel, where the warmth from the boiler below was so acceptable in this wintry weather.

'It's aye the same!', says Duncan. 'Ye're either gettin' ower muckle sleep, or nae half eneuch o't! A peety we canna store the stuff!'

'That mines me!', says Jeemsie. 'It's a peety we didna get mair stores in Lochinver; the beef's feenished! I'm aa richt for loafs, but there's nae beef ava. If we'd heen a gun, we micht ha' shot een o' yon deer that I see on the shore!'

'That mines me anaa!', says the Turk. 'Fin I wis a loon, I wis the finest shot in Scotlan'. I could dee ony mortal thing wi' a gun! I eesed t' ging doon t' the shows wi' a copper or twa, but I aye nott a barra t' hurl hame the prizes that I won at the shottin'! There wisna a bairn in aa the toon that didna hae a present fae me, aff o' the stallies! It feenished up that the show-mannie gied me a bob or twa t'bide awa, or they wid ha' been oot at the door! But, mine ye, I didna blaa aboot it!'

'Div ye think ye could shot a deer fae here, skipper?', says Duncan.

'Jist wyte or I hae a lookie, Duncan!', says the Turk, squinting along the barrel of an imaginary rifle. 'Och, aye! Nae bother ava! Mebbe nae jist smack atween 'er e'en, but certainly richt atween 'er lugs!'

'I thocht Buffalo Bill wis the only man that could dee that, skipper!' says Jeemsie.

'Weel, my loon, ye thocht wrang! It wis me that learnt Buffalo Bill t' hannle a gun. That wis fin Bill's father wis cox'n o' the Lonmay life-boat. Him an' me wis great pals!'

There was silence for a whilie, for very few men 'll tell their skipper, to his face, that he's jist a born leear.

'Fit's the name o' this loch?', says Duncan, to change the subject. 'I've nivver been here afore!'

'This loch', says the Turk, 'has a name that East-coasters canna pronounce, so I've aye caa'ed it "Abraham's Bosom"! Didn't I pick a richt name for't?'

'Oh, aye! Ye fairly did that! It's a gran' shelter!'

'Och! I've been here hunners o' times, Duncan. That little hoosie at the sooth end's the Post-office. It's jist a placie that sells tobacca an' pandrops, so we'll get nae beef here, cos there's nae anither shop ava! A mannie b' the name o' Hughie bides in that fite hoose at the ither end. I've kent him for mair than forty 'ear, an' I wid fairly like a news wi' the aal bodach again. We'll mebbe get ashore shortly, t' send a wire. Oor folk 'll be winnerin' aboot's, ye ken!'

'For God's sake, skipper!', cries Jeemsie. 'Dinna pit "Safe in Abraham's Bosom" on the wire, or my mither 'll tak a dwaam!'

Just after noon on the third day, the wind veered more easterly, so the Turk weighed anchor and brought the shippie alongside the little jetty, where she was securely moored across the end. Then our gallant hero made for the post-office, accompanied by Duncan and Jeemsie. No show without Punch!

A wire? That would be no problem, unless the telegraph wires were down! Beef? Provisions? Now, where do you think such things would come from, with the roads blocked solid for the past week, and likely to remain so for several days yet? Oh!, the locals had ways of surviving such conditions, but East-coasters were soft, and wouldn't know where to start!

1

'We're jist like the three bears!' says the Turk, as the trio made for Hughie's hoosie. 'Did ye ivver hear the richt story o' the three bears, Jeemsie?'

'No! skipper. Fit wye dis that ging?'

'Weel, my loon, they were a hairy lot!'

What a welcome they got fae Hughie! In a dolly-mixture of Gaelic and Doric and English, he bade them enter, and sit at the glowing peat fire. Jeemsie had never seen a room like this afore! From floor to ceiling, it was lined with tongue-and-groove timber, clear-varnished; the fireplace was whitewashed, as white as the snow outside, and a great muckle black kettle was hottrin' on the swye abeen the fire. They would take a cup of tea and a home-made scone? 'Aye! Surely: Fit could be better?'.

Then the older men began reminiscing on the distant days of Hughie's youth when, with a friend, he had walked all the way to Peterhead, to get a berth with the Turk's father, and had walked all the way home again, at the end of the season.

Jeemsie, who would normally have revelled in the old tales, never heard a word. His e'e wis rivetted on the gun hingin' on the waa.

'Dis that gun work, Hughie?' says he.

'Of course it works, my boy! I clean it regularly. It's an old, old friend.'

'Could ye shot a deer wi't?'

'Certainly! I would be efter a deer myself, but my eyesight's not so good now!'

'Could we get a len' o' yer gun, Hughie? We're gey short o' beef!'

'By all means, take the gun, but I've only three bullets left. It's not easy to get ammunition now, cos that's my old service rifle. I'll have to write to Ramsay MacDonald about it, to be sure!'

'Three bullets is plinty', says Duncan. 'In fact, ae shot wid dee wi' oor skipper; he's the finest shot in Scotlan'.'

Hughie gave his old friend a puzzled glance, but the crackshot was staring at the floor, showing little interest.

'Come awa, noo, skip! Now's yer chance! Richt atween 'er lugs!' cries the cook, takkin' doon the gun.

Eh, wah, wah! The peer Turk! He had t' be badgered afore he wid move! It wis ower caal, he wisna so young noo! Forty 'ear seen, maybe, but nae the day! But his protests were in vain.

An hour or so later, the three shipmates were leg-weary, wydin' amon' deep snaa. Fishermen's legs wis nivver made for mountains! Duncan had gotten the first shot at a deer, but it had been a waste o' time.

'Ach, Duncan! Ye couldna hit the parish ye wis born in!' says the Turk. The scorn in his voice was sharp and clear. Next to fail was Jeemsie, and the skipper's verdict, 'A miss is as good as a mile!'

'C'mon, noo, lads, it's time we wisna here! It'll seen be dark, so we'd better get back t' the ship. (Any drifter was aye 'the ship'). Fin we come t' the tap o' this brae, we should be lookin' doon on her.'

'There's still a bullet left, skipper!', says Jeemsie. 'An' look! There's a bonny beastie at the tap o' the brae. Here's the gun, aa ready loaded for ye. Ye ken yer crew's stairvin', so ye can hardly lat them doon. Richt atween 'er lugs, skip, the wye ye eesed t' dee't!'

Eh, the peer aal Turk! Fit wye could he tell them noo, that he had never fired a gun in his life? He jist couldna, so he took the gun, and steadied it on a rock. Then he took his tongue atween his teeth, steekit baith his e'en, an lat bleeze!

Boys! The deer lowpit sax fitt into the air, an' fell stone deid – on the wrang side o' the hill!

'Dalmichty! I nivver saw the like!' says Duncan.

'Nae sweerin'!' says the Turk.

Fin the three musketeers cam' pechin t' the tap o' the brae, the deer wis rowlin' doon the ither side, gaitherin' snaa like a snaaba'! An' she wis growin' bigger, an' bigger, an BIGGER! Lang afore she cam' t' the boddim, she wis as big as a hoose!

'Good grief!', says Jeemsie. 'If yon thing misses Hughie's hoosie, it'll sink the ship, for sure!' Then the trio set off doon the hill at a run. But, praise be, the only tree for forty mile saved the day, for the snaa-ba' struck the tree and burst open like a boom! Bowff!

I ken ye winna believe this, but, fin oor heroes arrived on the scene, they found, lyin' deid among the snaa, twa deer, three hares, an' forty-fower rubbits! Wi' the one single bullet! Good shootin', eh?

Duncan an' Jeemsie, fair dumfoonert, called the villagers to come and share in the spoils. Hughie was the first to congratulate the crackshot.

'How on earth did ye manage that, my friend?', says he.

'Och, that's naething!', says the Turk. 'Here's yer gun back, Hughie. If I'd heen a better gun, I micht ha' gotten a twa-three mair! Man, fin I wis a loon, ...'

'I could dee ony mortal thing wi' a gun! Mebbe nae jist smack atween 'er e'en, but certainly richt atween 'er lugs!', cries Duncan an' Jeemsie in unison!

Uncle Sam

When I was a boy, I had, on my father's side, no fewer than six uncles. This was entirely due to the prolificacy of the Buchan race; it had nothing to do with me. On my mother's side, I had a couple of uncles whom I saw but seldom, for the simple reason that they came from Stirling-shire and, in those days, that county was 'hine, hine awa!'. So, you see, for uncles I was stuck with the home-grown variety and, as nephews are perfectly entitled to do, I weighed each one carefully in the balance, merely to see which one I liked best.

After a great deal of heart searching, I decided that, compared to my Uncle Sam, the others were all rather colourless mortals. Uncle Sam was outstandingly different in that he was a most likeable rascal who could actually tell a story in Technicolour, and in 3D too. When Sam gazed at me from under yon shaggy eyebrows, and launched into a tale, Jason and the Golden Fleece, Scott of the Antarctic, and Big Chief Hole-in-the-Ground faded into obscurity, and I was away in another world. It is verily possible that my rapt attention encouraged him to gild the lily somewhat, yet never did I dream of doubting his word. Fact or fiction? What did that matter? It was good, it was spell-binding, it was magic!

By birth, Sam was 'een o' the Oxys', simply because his father was called Oxy, to distinguish him from all the other Andrew Buchans in the town. My own father was Oxy's Andra, and all his brothers were Oxy's So-and-so. Now, that should make me Oxy's Andra's Peter (see how it goes), or, if you like, Jeannie Motherwell's Peter, to distinguish me from all the other Peter Buchans. But, since both of these titles are a bittie unwieldy, I was given a handier name many, many years ago. The Oxy became Oxo, and I became Peter Oxo. Div I care! Fat lot o' difference it wid mak, if I did! So, in the Blue Toon, if ye speir, 'Faar dis Peter Oxo bide?', they'll pit ye richt t' my door!

Now, Oxy's Sam was a herring buyer, not a curer, but a 'fresher'. Freshers had little wooden boxes called 'margarines', eight margarines to the cran. These boxes were laid out in a long row on the pier, with a little ice in the bottom; then the fishermen would spread their baskets of herring evenly along the boxes, taking care to leave room for a sprinkling of ice along the top, before the lids were nailed down, when a fresh tier of empties would be laid on top of the first. It was a slow, scuttery job, discharging to a fresher. Ten cran made a 'dykie' of boxes, ten long and eight high, or vice versa. As soon as the boxes were filled, they were whipped off to the station to catch the south-bound train and, all the way south, at practically every stop, cadger's vans were waiting to uplift their orders. Thus were the fresh herring distributed throughout the country, all the way to Billingsgate in London.

Maist o' the freshers wore a white or khaki overall, and cairried a cloot for dichtin their han's; but Sam? Nivver! He jist dichtit 'is han's on's weyskit till he wis jist like a Pearly King fae Cockneyland. I never saw Sam in a hurry, I never saw him in a flurry, and I never saw him stuck for an answer.

To one English landlady, who asked if he was related to the Governor-General of Canada, who wrote *The Thirty-nine Steps,* he replied, 'Oh, aye! That's oor John, an aafa lad for writin' bookies!' And to another's query he replied, 'Haggis? Haggis, my dear, is what we Scots stuff our turkeys with!'. Now, I think he tellt a lee that time, cos I'm sure he nivver saw a turkey in his life!

Varying seasons found Sam in diverse ports, following

the herring. He was a proper kenspeckle character; he kent aabody, an' aabody kent him!

Behold him now, in a certain West-coast port in winter, immediately after the Hitler war. At that time, most of Scotland's whisky was being exported to the States to earn sorely needed dollars; thus customers in all the local hostelries were rationed to one glass, and one glass only, a rule that Sam didna like ava, for he likit a drappie! Since there were only twa places in the port, twa glaisses wis aa that a boddy could get, an' that wis jist nae eese ava t' Sam. So he set himself to devising a scheme whereby the niggardly 'one-glass' ration might be augmented.

There must be (or so he reasoned), many outlying hotels which, due to sheer lack of trade in the winter season, should be sitting on copious stocks of the amber liquid. Aha! He would hie himself thither to sample fresh delights! But, how was he to get there? He had no car, and, even if he managed to borrow one, he couldn't drive. And, to make things even worse, where would he get the petrol in a time of strict rationing? Alas! His castles in the air were crumbling at his feet!

Now, it so happened that the 'Minister of Fuel' in that particular port, had very little to do. (I mean the mannie that wis in charge o' the petrol coupons). There were as yet very few cars on the road, many vehicles having been laid up for years; and even to those who had cars in use, the meagre petrol ration was of little use in such a remote area. Thus, Rory the Coupon-mannie had plenty of time for a part-time jobbie on the pier, acting as helper to any fresher who might require his services. And so it transpired that he found himself one day working for Sam.

'Hey! Rory!', says Sam, dichtin' his fingers in the usual place. 'Div ye think a man in your position could spare a couponie or twa for the likes o' me?'

Rory was immediately suspicious. 'You know perfectly well, Sam, that I'm in a responsible job, and there are definitely no spare coupons. And, indeed, coupons would be no use to you anyhow! Where would yourself be going now?'

Rather reluctantly, Sam disclosed his great plan, and, to his amazement, Rory was quite enthusiastic.

'Och! man,' says he. 'If that's what's in your head, I'm sure I could find a coupon or two in a drawer, somewhere. And, if you're needing a driver, I'll do that as well. In fact,

we could go this very night, after we've had our one glass!'

So later that evening, we find our warriors in a remote inn, in the winter dark of a Highland glen, only to discover that the same old rule was in force. 'One glass only!'. Sam, rather disappointed, was ready to move on, but Rory was apparently in no hurry.

"Ochone, ochone!', cries he. 'It's an aafil world that we're after seeing now! A poor, poor place for those who have a drouth and a motor car, for there's neither whisky nor petrol to be had for love nor money!'

'Indeed to goodness, yes!' was the reply. 'There's not a bottle in the place, else you would be having it! And as for our car, it's been on blocks in the shed for years. We cannot get to Inverness to the pictures, and we've not seen Aunt Jessack in Achiltiebuie since the last three years or more. There's no petrol for pleasure motoring at all, at all, and it's weary we are in the winter without a break!'

'Sad. Sad indeed!' says Rory. 'No doubt you could use a few petrol coupons then?'

'No doubt whatsoever, but where would they come from, do you think?'

'I've got a few here!' says Rory, producing from his pocket a whole sheet of coupons. 'I'm the Petrol Officer at Portaloo, and these are a few spares I've come across in a drawer. They're yours, if you can find a bottle about the place!'

Goggle eyed, Sam watched the inn-keeper disappear into the back room with his prize. Then came the excited whispers, 'Portaloo Petrol Officer!'. Give them another glass, and fetch a bottle! Better make it two, and don't tell a soul!

Three more times that night did Rory work the Oracle, then, as they rattled their way back to Portaloo, the pair engaged in very earnest conversation on some remarkably deep subjects. Indeed, one confided to the other that it was his dearest wish that, someday, he would present the bairns of his native town with 'a poodlin'-pal far they could wyde in watter that wisna full o' slivvery doctors' (jelly fish). What a noble thought!

The cold, drizzly dawn found the bleary-eyed pair on the pier, Sam scutterin' aboot, levellin' oot the herrin' an dichtin' 'is han's in the usual fashion; Rory scatterin' ice an' nailin' on the liddies.

'Rory, my loon!', says Sam. 'I'm fair affrontit at last

nicht, but that winna help a lot, for it's you for the jile, an' it's aa my blame! I'm thinkin' ye'll get ten 'ear for ilkie couponie!'

Rory ceased his whistling of *The Drunken Piper* and, gazing earnestly at Sam, he says, 'Not to worry, friend! Not to worry at all, at all! They were all old coupons, completely out of date, and utterly worthless. I meant to burn them long ago!'

Now, if this is nae a true story, I canna help that. It's jist exactly as I heard it, near-han' forty 'ear seen!

But I hardly think Sam wid tell me a lee, specially wi' him bein' an Oxy!

Ferocious Pains

To use his own words, the Turk had the 'bonniest belly that ever braved the boisterous billow'. This pure, poetic gem was used only when some of his brother skippers teased him about his enormous girth. He had discovered that to reply in jocular terms was the best way to get peace.

'Oh, aye!', he would say. 'My taes is nae the only thing I hinna seen for a fyle!' Then, with a crude laugh, the jesting and teasing would cease.

But, secretly, the Turk was a 'wee bittie affrontit' at his corporation, though he made no effort to reduce it. It was common knowledge that the *Meadowsweet* had the biggest grub-bill in the fleet, mainly because of her skipper's insatiable appetite. Sliced bread was as yet several years in the future, and many a time did Jeemsie remark, 'My airms is sair cuttin' loaf till 'im'. Indeed, there had been the unforgettable occasion when Jeemsie had made a fly-cup for the skipper, who had just come off watch. Staring goggle-eyed at the two slices of bread left on the plate, the youngster had asked, in an unguarded moment, 'Fit wye did ye nae ait the hale loaf, skipper?', only to hear the good-natured reply, 'There's a mids in aathing, my loon, an' I've nae time for greed!'.

The Turk's own crew liked and respected him, as was amply borne out by their years of sailing with him. Not one of them would ever think of leaving him to seek another berth and, although they often had a quiet joke at the skipper's expense, the jokes were never malicious.

One day, while Duncan, the driver was helping Jeemsie to peel the tatties, the conversation turned to their lord and master.

'I'm thinkin' the skipper's nae verra weel 'iss days!', says Jeemsie. 'He's far ower ill-naitered for richtness!'

'Weel!', says his pal, 'Ye can hardly expect a chiel o' that size t' be aa weel at ae time!'

'I'm serious, Duncan! I'm sure the mannie's nae weel, an' I ken he has a lot o' pain at times. Last time I gid up t' the wheelhoose t' lat 'im doon till's denner, he wis fair grippin onto the wheel wi's belly!'

'Fit did ye say, Jeemsie?' Then, with a laugh, 'Oh! I see fit ye mean!'

'It's lefts-an'-richts, neeps-an'-tatties the day, Duncan, an' he'll scoff half o' the pot himsel'. I'll tak oot my ain share afore I ging up t' the wheel or there winna be naething left for me, fin I get back!'

As it happened, Jeemsie was dead right. The skipper wisna weel. For the past few trips, he had been sair bothered wi' severe pains in his digestive system, and this had him worried. Many a time had he worried when one of his crew had been ill, but now the worry was for himself.

'The nearest doctor's at least a hunner mile awa, an' that's a dizzen 'oors o' steamin at full speed!' The very idea gart 'im shiver! But finally, the Turk's good lady had read him the Riot Act, insisting that he should see the doctor.

Now, the Turk's vocabulary of nautical terms was very extensive, but when it came to medical words, he wis fair lost.

'What seems to be the trouble, skipper?' says the kindly physician.

'Weel, doctor, it's iss wye! I'm gettin' iss ferocious pains in my abomdemen!'

'I trust you mean your abdomen, skipper?'

'No! doctor, I div nutt! The pains is in my abomdemen!

5

Thats the fancy word for yer belly! I thocht ye wid ha' kent that, you bein' a doctor!'

The good doctor merely smiled, then proceeded to give the patient an extensive examination, questioning him astutely at the same time. After a thorough exploration of the Turk's great hemisphere, the verdict was, 'You're eating far too much, skipper, and you're eating it far too fast! You fishermen are all the same; you simply will not take enough time to your meals! Slow down a bit, or you'll have an ulcer very soon, and I can assure you, you won't like that!'

'Fit did ye say?', cried the Turk in alarm. 'An ulcer? A beelin' in my belly?' The fancy word had been forgotten.

'Not at all, skipper, I'll give you some white powder to take after meals, but, unless you follow my advice, you'll be in dire trouble!' This was followed by a short dissertation on the words, 'peptic', and 'duodenal', words which the Turk had never heard in his life.

'Qh, doctor!' says he. 'I'm aafa gled it's nae a beelin', an' I'm mair than thankfu' it's nae 'pendix!'

That night, the *Meadowsweet* sailed for northern waters, the intention being to fish with great-lines for cod, ling, skate and halibut, between the Orkneys and Cape Wrath. Bad weather was always a problem, and on this trip it was exceptionally coorse. There were no wireless sets on the fishing boats of that period, so the Turk had to be his own forecaster, and he was no mean hand at that trade. Years of experience had taught him to read the tell-tale signs of the clouds and the 'glaiss'.

On the morning of the sixth day at sea, the look of the sky, and the state of the barometer convinced the old salt that the best course of action was to seek shelter till the gale was past, and where better than in Loch Erribol, that great gash in Scotland's northern coast. It was a sair battered shippie, and a sair forfochen crew that gained the welcome haven in the early afternoon. As they entered the loch, Jeemsie was summoned to the wheelhouse.

'Noo, my loon', says the Turk. 'This crew's sair needin' mait an' sleep, so get the denner ready as fast as ye can! Naething fancy; bully beef an' tatties 'll dee, syne we'll aa turn in, an' jist lat her swing at her anchor.'

So, an hour or so later, we find the shippie safe at anchor in the shelter of the great loch, her crew fed and blissfully 'horizontal'. Jeemsie, having washed the dishes,

is about to creep into the cosy darkness of his bunk, when he hears a low moan from the skipper, who has gluffed his denner in his usual fashion.

'Ooh me, ooh me! The ferocious pains is back, my loon! The fite pooder's nae eese ava, so will ye heat a nammle plate an' pit it on the sair bit? They tell me heat's aafa gweed for a sair belly!'

So, up the trap goes Jeemsie wi' the plate, to heat it on the galley stove. He's back in a meenit or twa, wi' the het plate rowed in a sweat-rag, an' lays the thing canny on the sair bit.

'Ooh me, ooh me! That's richt fine!' says the Turk. 'Noo, the time that this plate's cweelin', wid ye nae be better t' heat anither een?'

The faithful cook duly obliges, up an' doon, up an' doon, but the pain's gey sweir t' shift!

'There's nae gaan t' be nae sleep ava for me the day!', thinks Jeemsie. Then, a flash of inspiration lichts up his face.

'By jingers!', says he. 'If it's heat that's nott, we'll seen sort that!' So, using the little lever supplied for the job, he lifts the lid o' the reid-het stove, an' plunks it square on the Turk's equator.

It is impossible to describe the scene which follows. Sufficient to say that, as the curtain falls, the peer Turk is on his back on the table, while Duncan, watched closely by a spellbound crew massages the reeking volcano with great dads o' margarine.

Jeemsie? Soon' asleep on his caff-saick!

The older generation in the area still recall 'the aafil day they heard the monster roaring in the loch. Indeed, it was an eerie sound'!

There wis a day or twa that the Turk didna speak t' Jeemsie. Wid ye blame him? But, strange as it may seem, he never had a ferocious pain aa the rest o' his days. In fact, he would advise everybody, whatever the ailment, to 'Hud on the heat'!

Mrs McTurk, however, had certain reservations which were clearly expressed when she met Jeemsie one day in Queen Street.

With a rueful sort of glance at her trinkle o' bubbly-nibbit bairns, she sighed, and she said, 'Oh, Jeemsie, Jeemsie? Fit wye di ye nae pit yon reid-het lid a wee bittie further sooth?'.

Ping Pongs

If you like fish and chips, the chances are that you have, at some time enjoyed a ping-pong supper. A ping-pong? Aye! That's richt, an' it's nae Chinese, for it almost certainly originated in Buckie, or maybe in the Sloch (Portessie). Let me explain.

In the years immediately following the Hitler war, the fishing industry was regulated by the Ministry of Food, a hangover from the war-time. No doubt the same thing applied to farming, but, whereas those appointed to run the fishing industry were invariably farmers, I never heard of a fisherman being appointed to run the farms. Od! They must ha' been fairmers, cos they could fairly pit the cairt afore the horse.

Now, there have been regulations regarding the minimum legal sizes for fish ever since I can remember, just as there have been minimum legal sizes for meshes. Every boat should have properly constructed gauges for the measuring of fish. A gauge is very easily made, for it is simply a little board, say 18×4 inches, with a stick nailed firmly across it, near to one end. Lines are then scribed across the board at distances varying according to the different species, say 10 inches for whiting, and 10½ inches for haddock. You lay the fishie on the board with her nose against the stick, and her tail must touch or cross the line drawn for that particular species. See? It wasn't possible to measure every single fish, but it's amazing how accurate the human eye can become, with just an occasional check.

Now, then, it came to pass that the Buchan Deep was swarming with haddockies, just a trifle short of the legal size. Mind you, they were bonny fishies, firm and plump, whereas those which were of legal length were thin, thin. Proper shargers. They were also exceedingly scarce! Wouldn't it be sensible to keep the short, plump fishies and discard the long, lean ones?

'This you cannot do! Ye'll get the jile for that!' says the Ministry.

'Aha!' says the Buckie mannie (but not to the Ministry, of course). 'If we clip their blastit tails aff, naebody can mizzer them. Nose to tail's the rule so, if there's nae tail …!'

Simple? Surely! Brilliant? Indubitably! Buckie? Ye may be sure! Thus was born a new breed of haddocks known as Ping Pongs, handled by a new breed of fishermen who became amazingly adept with a pair of scissors.

'Aha!', says the Ministry. 'We have seen Manx cats, but this is the first time we have seen Manx haddocks! Are they freaks of nature, in that they have no tails?'

'Na, na!', says the Buckie mannie. 'The peer craiters is chased t' daith wi' sharks, an' them that disna sweem fast eneuch losses their tails! It wid gar ye greet, so it wid. We jist tak' them aboord t' pit them oot o' their misery!'

Well, well, boys! It wis good while it lasted!

Now, in those days, there was no open vision (I Samuel 3:1). Many returning servicemen, wishing to become fish-buyers, found all sorts of bureaucratic barriers in their path. Then, when these had been surmounted, there was the personal hostility of certain buyers who had had 'the ba' at their fit' for six years, and wanted things to remain that way. That took some beating! Mind you, the fishermen wanted more buyers, the more the merrier, and during the awkward period many a box of ping-pongs was hoisted ashore in the dark, to give the newcomers a start.

Behold, now, two of these would-be buyer/merchants in the old fishmarket in the Blue Toon. For transport, Bill had a pram, and Fred had a message-bike. It had been a typical March day; gale force winds all day, falling calm after sunset. 'Sun down, wind down!' None of the PD boats had been at sea, so our two heroes were hanging about in the forlorn hope that some stranger might enter the port. And that's precisely what happened! A BCK boatie, which had been fishing near the Broch, came in and tied up in the darkest hole in the place!

'Hey!', says Bill, 'That mannie has ping-pongs, or he wid lie ower here far it's fine an' licht!'

'I believe ye're richt!', says Fred. 'We'd better hae a news wi' him!'

But the skipper, tho' quite friendly, wouldn't listen to their plea.

'It's been a wild day', says he. 'We jist got the ae drag afore the wither cam' doon on's. Half-a dizzen boxes o' ping-pongs on the pier there! I spoke ashore on the wireless, an' the wife's breether's comin' doon wi' a van for the fishies. He's fae Fitehills, an' he'll be here shortly!'

Not even the offer of an exceptionally high price would tempt him. In vain did Bill and Fred explain how the half of Buchan was depending on them for fresh fish on the morrow.

'It's the wife's breether, ye see! Nae my breether's wife. He has a chip shop, so he'll be needin' the fish. Come doon the caibin, an' get a joog o' tay the time we're wytin'. The van 'll seen be here!'

Some twenty minutes later, our heroes, refreshed but still disconsolate, resumed their pacing in the empty fish market. It was on the stroke of midnight, and they were about to call it a day when who should appear on the scene but Arthur, the runner cum ship's husband with one of the local salesmen.

Arthur was clad in his usual attire, a double-breasted, belted, military-style raincoat wi' strappies on the shooders. Faded till it was nearly white, the coat gave Arthur a rather dashing, distinguished appearance, something like yon chiel that can dee aa mortal thing, 'cos the lady loves Milk Tray'. Rather surprised to see the two pals, he bagan to sing in his rich baritone.

'Why weep ye by the tide, you twa?
Why weep ye by the tide?
Ye ken there's jist nae fish ava,
So here ye needna bide!'

'It's aa richt for you, Jock o' Hazeldene!' says Bill, 'But we're in a hole! Yon mannie ower there in the dark winna sell his ping-pongs t' hiz!' And out came the hale sad story.

'If I get the ping-pongs t' ye, is't worth a powen?', says Arthur.

'Oh, aye!', says Fred, 'I wid say it's worth twa!'

'C'mon, then! We hinna muckle time. Here's the van comin'!'

Now, then, Arthur stationed himself at the Brig, right underneath a lamp post, while Bill and Fred returned to the scene of their earlier failure, where the fishies were being loaded into the van.

'Ye're back again, lads!' says the skipper. 'Ye're wastin' yer time, cos here's the wife's breether for the fish!'

'Oh!', says Bill. 'We're nae seekin' the fish noo! We're jist doon t' warn ye that there's a Ministry o' Food mannie on the go the nicht, an' he swears that the first een he gets wi' ping-pongs 'll get sax month in the jile!'

'Dalmichty!', says the van driver. 'I didna see naebody fin I cam' doon the pier!'

'Weel!', says Fred. 'Ye'll see 'im noo! Look! Up there aside the lamp-post! Yon mannie wi' the fite coatie! "Sax month's jile", he says!'

Boys-o-boys! The boxes wis oot o' the van in five seconds, an' the driver lowpit inower an' pressed the starter.

'Hold on! Nae ower fast', says Bill. 'Drive canny fin ye're passin' the mannie, or he'll be suspeecious! Canny, noo!'

So the van crawled up the pier towards the Ministry mannie. When the van was just abreast of him, Arthur lowpit oot an' haimmered on the side o't.

'Stop, ye rascal!' cries he. 'It's sax month's jile for you!'

Nivver did a van ging ower the Brig at sic a lick! At least ninety, I'd say. Twinty meenits an' the driver wis happin' his heid in Fitehills. Nae bad for forty mile. 'If the bobby comes t' the door, I hinna been oot the nicht!' says he.

Helpless with laughter at the van's sudden departure, our two heroes turned to negotiate with the skipper, but lo, the boat was gone! She wis takkin' oot atween the piers wi' the verra sparks fleein' oot o' her starn!

'Sax month! Did ye hear yon? There's t' be nae mair ping-pongs aboord here! For God's sake pit oot that licht!', was the cry.

On the pier, a trio of still laughing pals surveyed the six boxes of fish which had been so hurriedly abandoned.

'We'll need a han' wi' this lot, Arthur,' says Bill. 'We jist hiv a pram an' a message bike. Fit aboot it?'

'I ken far there's a fine big barra!' says Arthur. 'But it'll cost ye three powen noo, seein' that ye're gettin' the ping-pongs for naething!'

'Three powen for the len' o' a barra?' cries Fred. 'By jingers, the Jews is nae aa in Jerusalem!'

The B.S.A.

'Peter Rennie eatin' fish, Alec catchin' eels;
Eels catchin' Alec's father eatin' raw peels.'

I'm sure that couplet will jog your memory as to what could be done with the word 'Preface' in a school text book. And, similarly, the 'Contents' could be construed as 'Cows Ought Not To Eat Neeps Till Sunday', although I've never heard that one in reverse order.

When one had acquired the knack of tripping such delectable phrases from the tongue, one had taken a tremendous step upwards on the educational ladder, a step infinitely more beneficial than any twelve-times table. Such is the mind of youth!

Today's generation is afflicted with a veritable host of abbreviations, such as TV, VAT, HP (not horse power) and Hi-Fi, to mention but a few of an endless list. On the other hand, my generation had very few abbreviations to handle, but, by golly, we certainly made the most of what we had! Of course we all knew about the English drifter which had been bought by Peterhead owners. Since her name was simply EJM, everybody thought 'They'll change that, surely!' But everybody was wrong! Her skipper, whose by-name was 'Mumphin', refused to change it, and to anyone who asked what the letters stood for, he replied, 'Everyone's Jealous of Mumphin'.

Then there was the Irish drifter which appeared on the scene bearing the name IFS (Irish Free State). The youngsters around the harbour soon changed that to I Feel Her Sinking, but she finally became *Accede* PD191.

We had a great deal of fun at times with abbreviations. If we knew what the letters meant, we lost interest immediately but, if the meaning was beyond us, we soon coined our own phrases to suit ourselves, the general rule being that, if we could make the meaning vulgar, it was sure to be good. If we could make the meaning unprintable, we had discovered a gem of purest ray serene!

One such gem stared us in the face every day as we left school, for directly across the road was Campbell's bicycle shop, which always displayed an attractive poster with the slogan, 'Lead the way on a BSA'.

Little did we know, and less did we care that the letters stood for Birmingham Small Arms, one of the finest cycle makers in the land, their trademark being three rifles stacked in a tripod. But it wasn't very long before some brilliant youth, whose name I never knew, produced a really unprintable connotation for the three letters. The new phrase was tested and tried, and finally pronounced good. In language which, I hope, is acceptable, the phrase simply meant, 'A gey sair dock!'. Rather innocuous after all, surely!

BSA bikes were British made, and were immensely strong, built to last. By today's standards, they were old-fashioned but, in their day, they were among the very best, although they shared a common fault in that they were rather high. It was quite common to see a boy riding a BSA, clinging to the side of the bike, with one leg 'through the bar'. They were as high as that. Only tall men could throw a leg over the saddle with ease. Men of medium stature found the feat rather difficult, and little fat mannies found it impossible.

But lo! A method was devised whereby the impossible might be accomplished, and this was simply by adding to the bike a 'back-step'. The back-step was merely an extension of the rear axle, usually on the left side, and the mounting procedure was as follows – (1) Take the bike by the handlebars in the usual way, then, with the legs, straddle the rear wheel. (2) Raise the left foot and place it firmly on the backstep. (3) With a Hopperty-kick motion of the right leg, push the bike forward until it gains a little speed. (4) Using the left leg as a lever, raise the body, just like going up a step. Now all your weight is on your left foot, on the back-step, and this weight must be swiftly shifted to the saddle. You'll know all about it if you miss the seat.

It wasn't everyone who could perform the act gracefully. It was 'better nor the picters' to behold some of the would-be cyclists mounting their steeds from the rear. Quite a few rolled their eyes skyward and gied a richt hairty sweer, if their contact with the saddle was on the heavy side. It was common to hear sundry gasps and grunts, and indeed, some of the more articulate riders announced to the public at large that they were off to Lipton's for cheeses. At least, that's what I gathered.

The ladies' version of these sturdy bikes was by no means without its problems. Specially for the young quines! You see, the handlebars were very much higher than the saddle, and this made it rather difficult for a lassie to steer with one hand. With one hand? Aye, surely! They nott the ither han' t' hud their hat, or t' keep their skirts doon for fear the loons wid see their bloomers. If only they could ha' seen themselves; most ungainly and unlady-like.

The real mistresses of these old bikes were the elderly country ladies who came into town with their black straw hats securely anchored, and with skirts long enough and heavy enough to defy a Force 8 gale. With torso erect on the saddle, with both hands on the handlebars, and with feet all but invisible, these ladies seemed to glide along, like black swans on a placid lake.

One owner of an ancient BSA was Dod, a 'vricht' fae Rora. In my early days, the country folk spoke of 'the vricht' as a man who could do any mortal thing. And indeed, many of these craftsmen were gifted with exceptional skills.

Such a man was Dod, a stocky, muscular chiel who had ridden his trusty old bike on more Saturdays than he could remember, to visit his life-long crony Sandy, in the fisher-toon o' Buchanhaven. In a boxie strapped to the 'carrier' just above the rear mudguard, Dod would bring to Sandy a bittie o' cheese or country butter, or maybe a dizzen eggs. On his return trip the boxie would contain a fry o' herrin', or a bittie o' fish, or even a raan (roe) if the season wis richt.

Dod and Sandy wid sit at the fire for an 'oor or twa, pittin the world in order, an', seein' that this wis a gey sair job, they nott a drap o' the Aal Kirk t'help them. Nae a lot, mind ye, jist a drappie! But ae nicht Dod wis richt fine pleased t' hear that Sandy's loon had come hame fae the Navy wi' a bottle o' Nelson's Blood (Navy rum) till's father. Oh, boys, the twa o' them had a rare nicht.

They nivver haard the twa fisher loons that took Dod's bike awa fae the door, nor did they ken that the loons cowpit the bike upside doon an' haimmered a hale box o' lang, blue tacks, een aifter the ither, throwe the seat!

Man, fin the loons put back the bike, the seat wis like a hedgehog.

Noo, than! Jist aifter dark, oot comes Dod t' tak the road hame. He wis steamin' a thochtie mair than usual, but och, he wid manage fine! He wid jist tak the bull b' the horns. This he did (fae the back, ye ken), an', wi' ae fitt on the back-step, he gid 'Oopie-up' an' came doon wi's usual clyte on the seat!

Oh, boys, oh boys! I dinna think it wid be richt o' me t' tell ye ower muckle aboot fit happened neist. I'm sure ye wid greet! But I'm jist as sure that there's nivver been a roar like yon since Hielan' Jess put her bust ower near the mangle!

The hale village cam' poorin' oot t' see this ferlie. 'Fit's adee wi' Dod the nicht? He's surely geen baresark! Did ivver ye hear bad words like yon? I'm sure that Tom Mix on his buckin' bronco couldna beat that performance!'

Little did they ken that Dod wis on 'is bike an' couldna win aff! At last, the peer tormented sowl got hud o' a lamp-post an' startit t' clim'. He had jist gotten a hud o' the crossbar at the tap, fin the bike let go an' fell t' the grun! Aa clear!

Now, at that time there was in the village a resident who had spent several years abroad, doon aboot Norwich or somewye lik' 'at.

'I think', says he, 'It would be expedient to fetch a doctor, PDQ!'

'Good idea!' says I. 'An' if he speirs, tell 'im it's a mannie wi a BSA.'

Noo than, a supergrass tellt Dod faa had meddled wi's bike, but Dod jist bided his time. Then, ae nicht, as he entered Sandy's hoosie, the aal fisherman says, 'There's been a terrible noise oot there this last fyowe meenits! Like somebody gettin' murdered, I wid say. Did ye see onything oot o' the wye, Dod?'

'Naething forbye, Sandy, naething forbye! I jist met in wi' twa loons, an I've gien the pair o' them a BSA, so that they'll mine on me lang aifter I'm awa!'

'Od!', says Sandy, 'Ye're gey gweed-wullie if ye gied them a bike the piece!'

'Na, Sandy, nae a bike! Nae a bike ava! Jist a gey sair dock!'

And he gied the taes o's tackety boots a close kind o' look!

Holiday in the Capital

According to Mrs McTurk, it wis a richt fine day for the fite thingies. The sky was brilliantly blue, and the few fleecy cumulus clouds were just as brilliantly white, while a light westerly breeze ruffled the golden grain on the broad fields o' Buchan.

Amongst the rich, dark greenery, the roddens were jist a bleeze o' reid, and the clean, sweet air was a joy to breathe.

'Ye'd better tak the gweed o' this, lads!', says the Turk to his crew. 'There's nae naething like this on the sea!'

The summer herring season had drawn to a close in the usual way. For a week or ten days, the number of spent (spawned) herring among the catches had gradually increased until finally the total catch was 'clean spent'. Then the shoals had departed to pastures new, and the herring fleet was tied to the pier. It was all over for another summer. Thousands of nets were bundled, to be loaded on carts and lorries which would carry them into the countryside, where the fishers would hang their nets to dry on any available fence.

On this particular day, the *Meadowsweet's* crew had been obliged to bring their nets five miles inland before they could find a vacant fence. They had actually passed a fence or two but, since they had been of the 'pykit weer' variety, they were not acceptable for the hanging of nets. Now, at last, they had found a suitable stretch of fencing and, as the heavily laden lorry (with solid tyres) drove slowly along the roadside, one man dropped the nets, one by one, along the grassy verge. His shipmates lowsed the bundles and hung the nets on the fence.

'Keep the spaces aiven, noo!', cries the Turk to the man on the lorry. 'An' for ony sake, dinna drap the nets amon' sharn!' Then, in a quieter tone, he says to Dumplins, the mate, 'Yon chiel that we spoke till said something aboot a fince. I hinna seen nae sign o' a fince, but I'm fine pleased we've gotten a palin'.'

'Aye, skipper, this is a richt palin', fine smooth weer, an' it's nae yon roosty kind either! It's a winner the fairmers disna compleen aboot nets on their palin's.'

'Och, they needna bother compleenin'', says the Turk.

"Wallace the Bruce passed a laa that fishermen could hing their nets onywye they likit!' But here the Turk was entirely wrong. The farmers were definitely not obliged to provide the fishers with drying facilities and, many years later, they were to make that fact abundantly clear, and rightly so.

Still, isn't it strange that, a few short years after the fishers were told to provide their own fences, there were no herring nets to dry. They were relics of a bygone day. Then the peer fairmers 'couldna get a bittie o' net t' hap the wife's strawberries'.

Now the nets that were being hung up on this bonny day would be taken in when thoroughly dry. Each 'man-wi'-gear' would take his own nets to his 'laftie' for mending and storing, but these nets would not go, in a week or two, to Yarmouth. No, the older, harder nets would suffice for the stormy shallows off East Anglia, where the risk of loss was so much greater.

As the squad made for the lorry which would take them home, the Turk again exhorted his men to savour the beauty of the scene. 'Tak' a gweed look, noo, an' maybe ye'll mine on't fin ye're punchin' oot o' Yarmouth river. There's nae mony days like this in a year!'

'Great holiday weather, skipper! D'ye nivver think on takkin' a holiday?', says Fairnie, one of the deckies.

Now, with a name like that, Fairnie was sure to be a stranger. Indeed, he was very nearly a foreigner, for, along with his chum Meldrum, he hailed fae Fisherrow, on the south side of the South Firth. Some skippers liked to have a couple of Lewismen in their crew, but the Turk preferred Sooth-kintra men.

'A holiday, Fairnie? A holiday? Holidays is for lawyers, an' bankers an' doctors, but nae for the likes o' hiz! A holiday? That'll be the day!'

'Lots o' folk in oor pairt o' the world taks holidays', says Fairnie. 'And they're jist ordinary workin' folk, miners an' dockers an' the like. Mind ye, they get nae pey for their holiday time, but they save up, the hale year, for their annual spree. An' they fairly enjoy it!'

'Aye! That's richt!', says Meldrum. 'An' I'm shair the

day's comin' when every man 'll get holidays wi' pey!'

'Good grief!', says the Turk. 'Holidays wi' pey? I've surely gotten twa idiots this time. Bolsheevicks, maybe!'

'I'll be hae'in a holiday masel' in a week or so,' says Fairnie. 'But I'm gettin' mairried first.'

'Mairried?' says the Turk. 'I thocht ye had mair sense! Is she a fisher quine? Will ye be hae'in a big feed!'

'No, skipper, she's no a fisher lass. She works in a jam factory, makin' the seeds for the raspberry jam! Ye ken – the kind that sticks alow yer teeth! It's t' be a quiet waddin', jist the twa faimlies, cos I dinna hae verra muckle money, ye see!'

'Peety!' says the Turk, 'ye should hae a richt fisher mairridge!'

'An' what d'ye mean by a richt fisher mairridge, skipper?'

'Oh!', says the Turk, airily. 'Cabs an' wine biscuits, an' a hurl hame in a hearse! Ho, ho, ho!'

That afternoon, Fairnie and Meldrum left for their homes in the south, on the understanding that the Turk would recall them by telegram in due course. At teatime, our gallant hero mentioned the silly word 'holiday' to his better half, expectin' that she wid hae a richt herty lach, but what a begick he got. Boys-o-boys, she didna lach! She fell oot on him instead, and I can tell ye, she didna miss him an' hit the waa.

'Holiday?', she cries. 'Awyte we'll hae a holiday! I've scrubbit fleers an mennit nets since ivver I saw yer face. I'm fochen deen wi' bairns an' hippens! I'm nivver awa fae the washin' tub! Ower the watter wi' a buttery cookie an' a bottle o' AI (lemonade)! Div ye caa that a holiday? The shippie winna sink, the world winna stop, if ye tak twa-three days aff! Holiday it is, m'lad, an' neist wik at that!'

Sufficient to say that 'neist wik', Mr and Mrs could be seen in Scotland's fair capital city, and the Turk hated it, just as his wife loved it. He wanted to see the Castle, and

something of Scotland's heritage, but it was, 'Aa richt, noo, but lat's see the shops first'.

Boys! She didna miss a shop, eence she got a start. It wis 'something till my mither, an' a thingie till oor Johnnie'. She even got a 'packet o' oots-an'-ins for oor Meg's hair'. Eh!, the peer Turk! He steed at the shop doors like a lost dog, dammert wi' the steer an' the heat, till, one afternoon a 'smairt-like deemie' spotted him as a stranger and a possible client. So she approached him with a certain proposition.

Now, the Turk wisna a feel aathegither! He had met this lassie's marra mony a time during the war, an' fine did he ken fit she wis aifter.

'Na, na, my quine!', says he. 'Wid ye nae be better t' look for a chiel a bittie younger than me?'

'Ye're no that auld!', says she.

'Mebbe no, lass, mebbe no, but I hiv jist the ae solitary powen in my pooch!'

'Oh, dear, dear!', says she. 'I'm afraid ye'll no get very much for a pound, these days!' And she left him alone in his glory.

Some ten minutes later, the Turk was joined by his good lady, empty handed for once.

'Come awa noo, darlin'', says she. 'We'll ging an' see the Castle, an' the Royal Mile, an' the model shippies in the Museum. Ye've been aafa good!'

Happy at last, our hero took his beloved's arm and guided her tenderly through the throng. Scarcely had they gone a hundred yards, when they met the 'smairt-like deemie', busy as usual in her quest.

One single head-to-toe glance at the Turk's companion brought a smile to the city girl's lips and, as she passed the Turk, she whispered in a remarkably accurate Buchan accent, possibly learned from a fairmer at the Hielan' Show, 'I tellt ye, Jock! I tellt ye that ye widna get verra muckle for a powen'!

Beldie's Maik

It was a glorious summer evening in the late twenties, the third Saturday in July to be precise, and the granite walls of the buildings on the north side of the Broadgate were warm from the unbroken sunshine of the long sultry day. Now the sun's rays were somewhat tempered by the haze of reek from the kippering kilns, a haze which shrouded the whole town in such windless weather. Not an unpleasant odour, that of kipper reek.

'Isn't it close the nicht?', said some.

'Aye! Gey smuchty!' was the reply.

The Salvation Army open-air meeting was in full swing, and an attentive audience of some two hundred listened to the bright music and song from a ring of around forty ardent Salvationists. 'I need no other argument, I have no other plea. It is enough that Jesus died, and that He died for me,' was the theme of their song. Real old-fashioned, Blood-and-fire, evangelical stuff.

Very few of the onlookers joined in the singing, mainly because they didn't know the words, and besides, it's not everybody that's at ease singing to the music of tooteroos, and in the street at that.

The congregation formed a most unusual throng, of diverse languages and customs, their common bond their fisher calling and their liking for the band. A really astute observer could quite easily have pinpointed each man's home port from the pattern on his home-knitted jersey. The Hielan'men, who were actually from the Outer Hebrides, had two, or maybe three brightly coloured buttons on the left side of their jersey collars, brilliant red or azure blue the favourite shades. Gaelic was their native tongue, and they used it freely when they were together. East-coasters' buttons were always black, and their speech was a rough-cut mixture of Scots dialects. Practically every village from Avoch to Berwick was represented on the Broadgate that evening and again, a keen ear could have traced a man's origins from the subtle inflections in his voice. The natives of Auch (Avoch) on the Black Isle had indeed a language of their own.

Most of the men were simply passing an hour or so until their wives or lasses would be released from the gutting-yards, for there had been a heavy landing of herring that day and the women were working late. A week-end at home during the herring season was something to be dreamed about; it could never be a reality. Lucky indeed, the local men, who could take their wives and bairns out for strawberries and cream on a Saturday night.

And then there were the Dutchmen, all in black, whereas the Scots wore navy blue. Quiet, decent men, the Dutchmen, broad in the beam and stoutly built like their luggers which lay at anchor in the Bay. These staunch Presbyterians had rowed ashore in their smaa-boats to spend an evening in the town; and how they loved to hear the Army! Among them there were several boys of school age, the envy of the local lads, for here were boys of our own age at sea with their Dads, in a foreign port, and with wooden shoes forbye! It jist wisna fair. Ye could aye pick oot the Dutchmen by their pleasant smell of scented tobacco and fried herring!

To complete the congregation, a bourachie o' local bairns kept bizzin' aboot like bum-bees; safe as ye like, for traffic was a thing unknown. Cars! What on earth were cars? Very informal indeed, the Army open-air!

Among the listeners was Beldie, a lass in her early twenties, neat and clean in hersel', but so shabby in her attire that she was verra near orra. Before her, she had an aul battered coach (pram) wherein sat twa bairns, nae jist ower clean, while a third loon clung to her skirt, sookin' 'is thoom. If every picture tells a story, then Beldie's was that of poverty. Fine did she ken far her man wis! In the pub for sure! And he wid come hame at nicht athoot a copper! Bill had faan oot wi's skipper in the middle o' the week and had left his ship, so, that mornin' at the office, he had gotten only half a week's wages. This he had keepit till himsel' for booze, an' he wid come hame sometime, clean skint! Fine did Beldie ken aa that, jist as she kent that there wis naething in the hoose t' gie the bairns. But wid she say a wrang word aboot Bill? Nivver!

Came collection-time, and a few lassies in Army bonnets mingled with the audience, rattling the coins in their tins as they went. One such lassie made as if she would by-pass

13

Beldie, but Beldie widna hear o't. It was 'Here ye are, my quine!', and into the tin went Beldie's worldly goods, one solitary maik (half-penny).

Daft, think ye? Aye, surely. A few minutes later, the band struck up a lively tune, and the Army marched briskly up the brae, followed by a motley straggle o' raggit bairns. Oh what fun to follow the band!

There was naething left noo for Beldie but t' ging awa hame, but first, she wid cry tee an' see her father an' mither. Fine did her father ken Beldie's sorras! Faa didna? An' sair wis 'is hairt!

'Hiv ye onything in the hoose ava, my quine!'

'Naething ava, Da, naething ava!'

'Weel, lass, we canna gie ye ony siller, but at least the bairns 'll get a piece here!'

And that was exactly what they got, loaf an' seerip, and hungrily they devoured it, afore Beldie left for hame.

Now, then, atween her father's hoose and her ain hame Beldie met her uncle, a weeda man, a droll hare that had nivver been kent t' gie onybody onything aa his days. A quaet man but grippy, grippy. Ye ken the wye o't.

But, this nicht, fin he saw Beldie wi' the drawn face, an' the bairns tryin' t' lick the verra hinmist mealicks o' loaf aff their fingers, he steed up wi' her and said, 'Here's a something t' yersel', lass. Something t' see ye ower the week-end'. Fine did he ken Beldie's sorras. Faa didna?

Nae till her uncle wis hine along the road did Beldie daar look at the coin thrust into her hand. She could hardly believe fit she saw! A hale half-croon! A complete fortin, an' fae him especially!

She wid need milk, so she ran hame for her flagon, for in those days, ye didna get milk in bottles. She wid need her time, for the shops wid shut at eicht o' clock, an' she couldna mak muckle speed wi' the bairns. But Beldie made it!

At the butcher's she got a bit bilin' beef an' vegetables for broth, an' a puckly sassidges forbye. In the little dairy shoppie she got milk, an' sugar, an' tay. Twa plain loafs, an' a great muckle pyoke o' broken biscuit, an' boys, she verra near forgot t' get tatties. Syne, best o't aa, maybe, the bairns got a sweetie!

The hale apothick gid inower the coach, an' jist as she came oot o' the dairy, the curfew bells in the Toonhoose began their eicht o'clock chime. Ony langer, an' she wid ha' been ower late!

It wis a different Beldie that took the road hame. She seemed t' be lifted up! Mait for a day or twa, what a blessin'! She even managed to hum a tune she had heard the Army playin'.

But still, boys, the day wisna deen, for, along the road a bittie, Beldie met a spinster cousin, a sour, lonely kind o' woman whose weekly practice wis t' tak t' the cemetery a little rooser t' water the flooers on her mither's grave. Fine did she ken Beldie's throwe-come! Faa didna? But little did she care! Beldie should ha' heen mair sense in the first place! Bill? Wah, wah!

An' yet, fin she saw Beldie's smilin' face, fin she saw the laden coach wi' the bairns clocherin' an' sneezin' at sherbet-dab, she couldna help saying', 'Beldie, my quine, it's a pleasure t' meet ye. Ye're the first happy an' contentit face I've seen the nicht. Here's a something t' yersel'!' And into Beldie's han' she shivved a twa-shillin' bit. Beldie's cup wisna full; it wis rinnin' ower!

Now, maybe ye're thinkin' that this is a religious tear-jerker o' a story. It wis nivver meant t' be that! Ye see, the truth aye tells twice!

'Weel!', ye micht say, 'I canna see onybody gettin' aa that mait for half-a-croon!'

In the twenties ye could! Nae bother ava. Ye see, the powen wis worth something in yon days.

An' fit gars ye dibber-dabber aboot the half-croon, onywye? Did she nae get the hale lot for a maik?

Beldie thinks she did!

Hilly's Pension

It took me quite a while to get really close to Hilly, but that was entirely Hilly's blame, for he was forever roarin' and bullyin' about something or other. Even when he was simply commenting on the weather, he made more noise than I could make with a loud-hailer and, when the weather didn't suit him, his voice was like the trump of doom.

When I first met Hilly, I got the impression that his belligerent tone was the direct result of his taking umbrage that I, a stranger, should have the temerity to trespass on his ground at all. As time went on, however, I perceived that he addressed the world in general in the same blustering fashion, and this made him, in my eyes, an uncouth loudmouth, a bag of wind. Then, quite by accident, I overheard him speaking to his little, orphaned granddaughter in tones that would have shamed a cushie doo. There was a hidden tenderness about the man, a something completely at odds with his warlike utterances. Was it possible that Hilly was a loving, caring man, afraid that the world might discover that fact?

As was to be expected, Hilly soon discovered that I was from the sea and, from that day, his bark wasn't quite as fierce, his whole attitude a trifle softer. Mind you, it was a slow, slow thaw, but we did eventually become quite friendly. The last of the ice was completely shattered the year that Hilly had his bumper crop of Golden Wonders. Whether or not he had a bigger crop than he was legally entitled to have, I simply don't know. That was none of my business. But he did seem to have an embarrassment of riches, some of which he was anxious to be rid of, without actually throwing them away. And in me he found a friend in deed, for I could dispose of a considerable amount of Goldies among the fisher folk who, as everybody knows, are gey fashious aboot tatties. Mony's the bag o' Goldies that I bought at Hilly's; terms strictly cash! And, should I call at the farm in his absence, I was at liberty to help myself from the tattie shed, and 'leave the siller in yon tinnie that's on the easin' o' the waa'! On no account was I to give the siller to Mrs Hilly. That too, was none of my business, but I did discover that, with this

'kitty' in the tinnie, Hilly bought surprise gifts for the bairn. You see, the tinnie stood on top of a mail-order catalogue whose pages were immaculate, apart from the 'Children's Gift' section. There the pages were filthy, and a few inky crosses opposite certain items betrayed Hilly's secret. I'm sure nobody knew of this side to Hilly, and certainly nobody heard of it from me. Mrs Hilly did once mention to me that 'He aye winners faa the Hell's this that's aye sennin' presents t' oor bairn'! She leuch, quaet kind, then she says, 'He surely thinks I'm a feel, but I jist lat him be'!

Came the day when, over a fly-cup, Hilly asked if I knew anything about sailing-ships. I had to confess that, apart from what I had read, I knew very little indeed, whereupon he took me ben the hoose to a spare room which had been turned into a sort of study. The walls could scarcely be seen for the beautiful paintings and photographs of the China clippers, the wonderfully graceful ships which carried great cargoes of tea from the Far East. *Cutty Sark* and *Thermopylae* were well to the fore and, in a bonny rosewood book-case a profusion of beautifully bound books with gold lettering took the eye. Every one of these volumes had to do with sailing ships and their history. So this was Hilly's secret passion! Strange hobby for a hill farmer who had never been afloat in his life.

Were I to mention a ship's name, Hilly could tell where and when she was built, with details of any subsequent changes in ownership or nationality. From memory, he could give me the precise position of the *Cutty Sark* when she was dismasted in a storm in the Roaring Forties and, along with that, he could name the Captain and the two apprentices who were on watch at the time. Hilly was a walking encyclopaedia on the era of the windjammers and, strangely enough, a very quiet-spoken man at the same time.

I managed to tell Hilly how a windjammer, on shipping a great sea over the stern, filling the decks level with the tops of the bulwarks, could have up to 1500 tons of water on her deck. I also managed to tell him that the windjammers were not all ships, for a ship is 'A three-masted

15

sailing vessel, square rigged on all three'. He was simply delighted at receiving this information, which he had apparently missed in his reading. No! I'm not a fountain of knowledge on that or any other subject. The two 'nuggets' which I passed on to Hilly were simply part of the heterogeneous mass of useless facts which clutter my memory. I'm just like you – I could easily be Mastermind if only Magnusson would ask the proper questions.

Despite his vast store of knowledge, Hilly had never heard of the clipper Captain who was a stickler for Divine Service on a Sunday morning. While it wasn't compulsory, most of the crew, as their duties permitted, would gather on the after deck to hear the Captain read a portion of Scripture before engaging in sincere and earnest prayer. This was a pleasant break in the awful monotony of a voyage which could take four months. Now, as long as the weather was warm and kind, the Captain had a substantial and attentive audience but, as the ship reached ever further south toward colder climes, the congregation dwindled steadily, until only one worshipper turned up. That morning, in showers of hail and sleet, the service was unusually brief. Then the Captain invited his lone disciple into his stateroom and gave him a 'hale tumbler o' fuskie'. Consternation reigned in the fo'csle when the wanderer returned, for the smell of spirits on his breath aroused fierce longings in the hearts of seamen who hadn't savoured such an aroma for months.

Needless to say, but on the following Sunday the Service was a packed house, even though icicles hung from the rigging. But there was no welcome stirrup cup to cheer the weary mariners on the way back to their quarters. As the Captain was about to disappear below, an aggrieved voice cried, 'Is there nae gaan t' be a drappie the day, Captain?'

'No!', says the skipper. 'Nae even the smell o' a drappie! An' if it's last week that's botherin' ye, let me tell ye that last Sunday was Communion Sunday!'

'Fit wis the ship's name?', says Hilly, mesmerised.

'I canna mine that,' says I. 'But the skipper wis a McKay fae Portsoy, and the chiel that got the drink wis a Coull fae Portgordon.'

'I wid say that proves the truth o' the story!', says Hilly, lachin'.

The day came when, in passing, I noticed that somebody had 'howkit oot a foon for a new hoose', on a bit roch grun

nae far fae Hilly's hoose, so I called in to see him.

'Are ye gettin' folk t' bide aside ye?' says I.

'Na, na!', says he. 'That hoose is for me an' the hen!' He nivver said naething aboot the bairn, but I assumed that she was included. 'I'm retirin' this year, so I thocht I'd mak' some eese o' yon grun'. It hisna been ony eese for a lang time noo! But man, I'm hae'in an aafa job gettin' the Pension. Ye see, I wis born on Boxin' Day, but it wis weel into January afore my father could get into the toon t' register my birth, there wis that muckle snaa at the time. Apparently somebody made a mistak' wi' my birth certificate, for it's a hale year wrang. I'm tellt I've a hale year t' wyte yet. They jist winna listen t' me ava, unless I can get witnesses t' prove them wrang. Faar's a man o' my age gaan t' get witnesses t' prove his date o' birth?'

'Ye're nae needin' witnesses!' says I. 'A certificate for the 26th o' December, if it's made oot in January, maun refer t' the year afore, surely!'

'I've somebody workin' on that noo!' says he. 'I'm tellin' ye, naething on earth 'll stop me fae gettin' that pension. I'm nae wytin' a hale 'ear for naebody!' Hilly was back to his former roarin' self again.

I wished him the best of luck and, a few nights later, he 'phoned me with the glad tidings that the mistake in the old records had been discovered, and he would get his pension. 'But it'll tak them a meentie t' sort aathing oot!'

'Fine!', says I. 'Jist gran'! I'll be up some day neist wik for a puckle mair tatties. Is the tinnie aye on the go?'

'Oh, aye!' says he. 'Aye on the go. If I'm nae aboot, ye ken fit t' dee. But nivver say boo, nivver say boo!'

When I did get around to calling for my tatties, Hilly wisna t' be seen.

'Och!', says I t' mysel', 'He's likely awa seein' aboot 'is pension.' And I took my tatties as before.

But, boys, there wis nae tin, an' there wis nae catalogue. Hilly wis surely naeweel, so I made for the hoose an' cried in at the door, 'Faar 's the man the day, that he's nae shoutin' an' roarin'? Is he lyin'?'

'Oh, aye!', says her ain sel'. 'Awyte he's lyin'. Lyin' ben the hoose in's coffin!'

Boys, oh boys, ye nivver ken!

Me? I put the tatties back in the shed and nivver said boo, nivver said boo.

But I grat a bittie on the road hame.

The Chancer

Solo was a lifelong member of that illustrious band of fishermen known as the 'Chancers', or the 'Chance Shot' brigade, a sort of necessary evil in the fisher communities. It is quite possible that their title varied from port to port, but I'm sure that every port had its quota of such characters, the lads who were never very long in the same ship although, at the same time, they were never very long idle. In these fellas, the skippers had a sort of reservoir of casual labour which had its unofficial headquarters at the Lazy Dyke. It would not be uncharitable to call them birds of passage, here today and gone tomorrow, unwilling to be bound by any local customs or usages. (There were no rules and regulations).

Now, having said that, I should point out that, among the chancers there were some good hands whose only apparent fault was their roving disposition. There were others who were poor hands at their trade, and would never be any better. Then there were those who were just downright lazy, and they, too, would never be any better. I once heard a Fifer describe the latter category as 'one-gallus lads', and I thought the title was rather apt. It also proved the point that the chancer is a ubiquitous species, both ashore and afloat.

Solo, however, belonged to neither category. He was something of a 'one off' job in that he was such a likeable bloke. Any skipper looking for a man to fill a gap in his crew counted himself rather fortunate if he managed to enlist Solo, on the strict understanding that the limit of his stay would be one week. Less than that, maybe, but certainly never longer. You know, the vacancies caused by bereavement, or sickness, or whatever. And, quite often, Solo was better than the man he replaced.

Solo acquired his nickname in the 'thirties, when open-air gambling schools were so common. Groups of unemployed youths would gather in sheltered, secluded spots where look-outs could be posted to warn of any arrival of the police, and all sorts of card games took place. Ditto with bingo (housey-housey) which, at that time, was strictly illegal. Well do I remember the day when three little boys, playing on a raft of planks and oil-drums in the old dry dock, met their fate. The raft had overturned in some three feet of water, and only one of the boys managed to reach the steps. Panic-stricken, the poor lad ran all the way home to tell his mother, unaware that, less than fifty yards away, behind the dyke, some forty men were playing 'housey'. Sad to say, help came much too late. Such, they say, is life.

Elsie Jean, Solo's dear wife, saw to it that he was always clean and tidy, whether he was in or out of a berth. She was, I believe, a native of the Sea-toon o' Cullen, where cleanliness is, literally, next to godliness. If there were any niggling doubts about Solo's willingness to work, there were no doubts whatever about Elsie Jean, for she was a proper human dynamo. Scrubbing, cleaning, gutting herring or mending nets, the deemie was never idle. Although they had no family, the couple were supremely happy, with only one fly in the ointment, – there was no way that Elsie Jean, a staunch Christian could get Solo to the Kirk. He had no time whatsoever for religion, and wasn't slow to advertise the fact.

Some of the many skippers with whom Solo had sailed would have been both willing and able to discuss with him Christ's Sermon on the Mount, or the teaching of the Apostle Paul in any of the Epistles, but Solo simply wasn't interested. He would rather speak to the motion that all boat-owners, skippers, and men-wi'-gear were blasted Capitalists, 'sookin' the hired men's bleed'! Such an unorthodox dogma convinced most skippers that Solo was 'jist a Bolsheevick'!

A born philosopher, Solo would not willingly take a temporary berth with a skipper who was doing well, simply because such a man was certain to be due for a 'duff' week. Conversely, a skipper who wasn't doing well at all was considered a safe bet. Under this personal gambling system, Solo had sailed with most of the local skippers and, on the whole, he did quite well, albeit he was 'jist a hired man'.

Like so many others of his generation, Solo chewed Bogie Roll; a filthy habit which Elsie Jean simply wouldn't tolerate in the house. You see, those who chew tobacco have an unbelievable amount of saliva to dispose of, so they are not the best of company in the domestic world. Thus Solo was obliged to pursue his obnoxious habit in the great outdoors, where he could spit to his heart's content. Sorry! I misrepresent the man. Solo never spat; he simply ejected, from between his teeth, a long, needle-thin jet of dark brown fluid. Fsssst! His aim was deadly, and I have seen him extinguish a candle at the first shot from ten feet away. Of course, that was no redeeming feature!

I have often heard it said that each one of us has some special talent. It may or may not be dormant, but nevertheless, we've all got a something. Well, Solo's special gift lay in his ability to remove a herring scale from a boddy's eye.

The herring scale can be a terrible irritant to the human eye. It is transparent when wet, so it becomes invisible on the eyeball. Its very nature makes it cling, so it is extremely difficult to remove, but Solo knew how to do the trick! He would go 'Fsssst', then he would temporarily remove the 'chaa' from his cheek prior to laying the patient flat on his back. Then, all ready for action, Dr Solo would use his sophisticated instruments (fore-finger and thumb), to open wide the afflicted eye which he proceeded to wipe clean with his tongue. Primitive? Well, maybe a wee bittie! Efficacious? In every case! But, oh boys, the tongue felt like a file, and the 'bacca bree stung like fire for a whilie. Still, that was but a slight affliction.

Another chap, whom I know very well, had a similar cure; but, instead of his tongue, he used the well-nibbled end of a match. Nae bother ava! An' him wi' fingers like mealy puddens, tee! These are the times when you must have great faith in your fellow slave, whether he chaws tobacca or no!

Came the joyous day in Elsie Jean's life, when she finally managed to get her man to the Kirk, for the first time in his life. Trim and spruce in his best go-ashores, he gid into the seat afore Elsie Jean (nae mainners, ye see), an' sat close to the waa, wi's legs hard against the het pipes, an' his heid hard against the plaister. But, boys-o-boys, he forgot to tak' the chaa oot o's mou. Verra seen he wis needin' t' 'Fsssssst', but far could he 'Fsssssst' in the kirk? Doon the back o' the pipes, far else?

Kirk or oan kirk, Elsie Jean fell oot on him.

'Ye fool, orra, slivvery, Blue Toon tink! Div ye nae ken ye're in the Lord's Hoose? Try that again, an' I'll feenish ye. Ye're nae gaan t' affront me!'

Sensing that this was no idle threat, Solo got the chaa into his hankie, and stowed it in his pooch.

Now, in yon days, in yon Kirk, the offering was taken up in great muckle open pewter plates, not in velvet baggies, as is the present custom. As it happened, Solo was the very first to have the empty plate offered to him, then, looking the steward straight in the eye, he says, quaet-kind.

'I'm nae needin' that, freen! I'm stoppit spittin' noo!'

I miss him at the Lazy Dyke! The chancer!

Pirates from the West Coast

From Campbeltown and Carradale and Tarbert-on-Loch Fyne and from Girvan and The Maidens on the Ayrshire coast they came. Through the Forth-and-Clyde canal they came to raid the Firth of Forth, these pirates from the west. Under the great Forth Bridge they sped on the ebb tide, and like a swarm of locusts, they made for that stretch of water which lies between Elie Ness and Fife Ness, a rectangle of sea comprising the waters from half-a-mile to some four miles from the shore; the fringe of gold on the beggar's mantle.

For many, many years prior to the Hitler war, shoals of herring, dense at times, had sought these waters in February, March and April. We called them 'winter herrin'' but, before the shoals grew really dense, it was really

Spring and, very shortly, the herring would seek shallow water to spawn before disappearing for another year.

This, then was the treasure sought by the armada from the west. They had every right to be there, those rascals with the peculiar registration letters, CN (Campbeltown), TT (Tarbert) and BA (Ballantrae) on the Ayrshire coast. They were simply Scottish fishermen, seeking a share of Scottish herring but, as soon as they rounded Elie Ness, they met a wave of hostility which is hard to understand. How the St Monans men hated the ring-netters from the west! They would finish the winter herrin'; they would sweep the Firth clean, with their murderous nets! They should be completely banned! In fact the ill-will grew so strong that the St Monans men refused to allow the 'ringers' drinking-water, so the West-coasters went to Anstruther, where a more liberal attitude prevailed. Then the St Monans men fell out with the 'Enster' men, just as they had fallen out with the Pittenweem men, for refusing to refuse water and other commodities to the strangers. There were some really ugly scenes, but gradually tempers cooled, although the St Monans men never really lost their ill-will towards the 'pirates'. Indeed they set about collecting a great deal of hard evidence against the West-coasters, very hard evidence indeed, for it consisted mainly of lumps of lead, and reels of piano-wire.

You see, there's a world of difference between drift-net and ring-net fishing. The drift-net boats would shoot their long curtain of nets (about 40 nets), and lie for an hour or two, in the hope that some herring would swim into the meshes. Then they would haul in the nets, clean them out and shoot them again somewhere else, if the first haul had been unsuccessful. Indeed sometimes the nets were hauled three times without success. It was a slow, laborious, haphazard method of fishing, for no matter what happened, the herring HAD to swim into the trap.

The ring-net was a different Maggie Rennie altogether, in that it required a heavy spot, or shoal of fish which it could 'ring' or encircle. Once such a spot had been found and rung, the net was slowly drawn in, until a great seething mass of herring was imprisoned alongside the boat, then the process of 'brailing' began. The brailer was a huge, immensely strong butterfly-net affair on the end of a stout pole which was thrust down into the living mass. Then the great iron ring at the mouth of the brailer was dragged on board and jammed just inside the bulwark, a rope from the winch to the bottom of the bag took the strain, and 'Hey-presto', a cran or two of herring were 'cowpit inower onto the deck, where they flooded in a ripple of silver into the hold. The process was repeated until the net was empty; then, if necessary, another ring would be made.

Now, how did these highly efficient fishers locate the spots or shoals? Well, every boat (they always worked in pairs), had a 'feeler', a lump of lead roughly pear-shaped, which was towed slowly along, close to the sea-bed on the end of a long reel of piano-wire, usually double. The man who sat in the stern holding the wire, could feel the herring strike the wire; he could tell whether the fish were in quantity or not, and if the wire encountered a dense shoal, the wire would be very difficult to hold. In those days, when sonar, echo-sounders and fish-finders were utterly unknown, the wire feeler was a simple but effective tool. Now, in such congested waters, with boats from near and far spread all over the place, it was inevitable that some of the lead sinkers would foul the drift-nets, some of which were torn as a result. Now any drift-net man finding a 'feeler' in his nets could have kept it as a feeler for his own use; but no! Most of the offending objects were taken ashore to swell the mountain of lead which was being stored as vital evidence of the havoc wrought by the ringers. Nothing ever came of that lot; the war saw to that.

For ten winters, prior to the war, we fished the Firth in our family forty-footer, *Sparkling Star*. St Monans was our base, not because we liked the harbour (which was terrible), but simply because we had some life-long friends there. Every family had its own erection of spars for the drying of nets, either in the back-yard or up on the 'Mare' (common) which was a veritable forest of old masts. Most families had a barra for taking torn nets up fae the shore an' takkin' hale nets doon. Indeed, a barra was a most acceptable wedding gift! Torn nets there were in plenty, most of the damage being caused by the great steamers leaving Methil with cargoes of coal. A steamers propeller can make a fearsome mess of a net, and usually takes away a great part of the sheet. The patch required for the repair was, in St Monans parlance 'net-bit', and was as a rule handled by the women-folk. So expert were they that their men scarcely had to handle a net at all, apart from the shooting and hauling. In fact that was about the only time some of the men saw nets at all. Lucky, lucky chaps awyte!

Now, these grand fellas had a custom whose marra I have never seen anywhere else. Fishermen of my generation (and older) would normally pace to-and-fro, side by side as they conversed on the pier, but on the Middle Pier at St Monans they would form little groups of four, all facing inwards, and step back-and-fore. Thus one walked backwards while his oppo stepped forwards, and the men at each side took a few steps sideways, every man with his hands deep in his pockets. At regular intervals the group would move 'one notch' to the right so that everyone got a change of step. No doubt they were unaware that I, a stranger found the practice completely fascinating and absolutely hilarious! Try it sometime and see.

The old men of the village took a deep, kindly interest in our welfare. We were the strangers within their gates and as such we were accorded the utmost civility and the warmest of hospitality. The spick-and-span appearance of these 'auld yins' proclaimed that loving care was in bountiful supply. Of course, they weren't really strangers at all, for they kent mair o' my ain toonsfolk than I did mysel'. Hadn't they been gaun t' the 'Drave' (the summer herring fishing) for as long as they could remember? Fine did they ken the ancestry of every one of us, for had they not fished at 'Yermuth' with our fathers? Then they would reminisce how, in the distant past a 'fairmer fae King's Barns wid come roond the fishin' villages on 'is horse, ringin' a bell an' shoutin', 'There's herr'n i' the Hakes! There's herr'n i' the Hakes!' Now, the Hakes is a stretch of water just below King's Barns so it is actually in the Firth of Tay, and not in the Forth at all. Nevertheless, every year towards the close of the season, the herring came there in unbelievable numbers, and it was the frantic activity of the sea-birds that told the fairmer there was 'Herr'n i' the Hakes'. And they could be jist like a dyke!

I remember vividly one particular night of very dense fog; it must have been thick indeed, for we were the only boat to put gear in the water that night. By making a wide detour to ensure that we were well clear of the North Carr light-ship and the dangerous reef which it marked, we literally groped our way into shallow water near King's Barns. In those days aids to navigation were unknown, so it was more or less guess-work, or shooting blind. Well, in any case, a bonny clear mornin' found us hauling a 'richt heavy strag' from the ten nets we had anchored. It was murderous work for five men (the sixth was in the little wheel-house, steaming the boat ahead as required), but we were young and fit and very hungry for herrin'. The very last net was a richt sair fecht, hauling up to the anchor through a strong tide, so we hailed the *Crest* PD.9 which was making empty-handed for port. By golly, the Boddamers didna tak' lang t' lift that anchor, then they yokit t' haul the net fae the ither end, so that the twa boaties lay thegither in the calm, and twa crews were haulin' at the same net. I reckon there was ten cran in yon net; she wis nivver ony mair eese. Fifty-seven cran we landed that day, oot o' ten shallow nets, athoot the fower-an-a-half cran that the *Crest* got. An' sic a price we got, tee! Forty-twa shillins the cran! That's twa powen ten pence, nooadays. Surely I've made a mistak' somewye, 'cos ye'll pey five bob for a kipper noo!

But freen, we've gotten wannert awa fae the subject, tho' that's naething new. Far's the herrin' noo? 'Och,' says you, 'They're awa in half-cran Klondyke boxes to Altona'. Fine div ee ken that's nae fit I mean! Far's the herrin' noo? Fit wye is't that there hisna been a herrin' seen in the Firth nor the Hakes since the middle o' the war? Wis't the ring-nets that feenished the Firth?

I jist dinna ken, but I'll tell ye ae thing for sure; the East Neuk o' Fife 'll nivver be the same athoot the herrin'.

A meenit ago, I wis speirin', 'Far's the herrin?' Noo I'm speirin', 'Far's the folk?' The herrin' didna ging awa their leen; they took a hale race wi' them! 'Fisher villages,' did ye say? Weel, far's the fisher folk?

Mony a time div I ging back t' the East Neuk, through King's Barns to Crail syne wast to Cellardyke/Enster an' Pittenweem to feenish up in the aul' hame, Si Minnins (St Monans). Boys, I likit yon folk!

I nivver see a fisher face; I nivver hear a fisher word. Oh, I see the fisher hooses still there, but I'm gey feart it's strangers that's in them.

The Fisheries Museum? Aye, surely, at the first o't, but nae noo! It jist gars me greet!

I wid far raither see a fleet o' pirates fae the Wast side comin' doon ower Elie Ness on a Monday aifternoon!

Nae Dubs aboot the Door

Great Stuart Street in Peterhead is a narrow, unpretentious cul-de-sac which lies back-to-back with the houses on the south side of Port Henry Road. The street, of whose existence the major part of the town is blissfully unaware, contains nine houses, stoutly built of the local red granite. The houses were built to a standard pattern, with two rooms and a middle closetie downstairs, and two large rooms upstairs. At the rear, each house had a 'back-hoosie', brick-built, and back-to-back with that of its next door neighbour. These back-hoosies usually served as washin'-hooses, very popular at night with courting couples. Toilets came on the scene many years later, and were always outside, in the backclose which afforded barely enough room to swing a cat.

I believe the builder's name was Stuart, and he named the street after himself and also after a famous street in Edinburgh. A private joke, maybe.

But, in any case, apart from official documents, Great Stuart Street has never been accorded its illustrious title. Generations of fisher-folk have called it the Burnie Streetie, simply because its very first occupants were 'Burnies', incomers from the little fishing village of Burnhaven, a straggle of 'butt-an'-bens' on the north shore of Invernettie Bay, often called Sandford Bay. In such desperately humble beginnings do so many of today's prosperous fisher-folk have their roots. I use the word 'desperately' quite deliberately, for in Burnhaven poverty was the name of the game, and abject poverty at that. Oh, I know that today's race have a jolly good laugh at some of the tales about the Burnhaven days; they seem to think that such conditions are a figment of older folk's minds but such is not the case, and for this I have as witness the words of my own father, who was born and bred a Burnie.

Take a good look at your eleven-year-old son, if you have one; take a look at any eleven-year-old boy, and tell me how you would rate his chances as cook for eight men on a sail-boat, and away from home too! That's exactly what my father had to do, as the eldest of a family of nine.

In those days, the fishing boats carried their beef with them, salted into casks, when they went to Shetland. As cook, it was my father's job to take from the cask sufficient beef for the dinner and hang it over-side to steep. The sea water, though salty itself, would still remove most of the salt from the meat. Well, one day in Lerwick, whether by accident or not, the string was cut, with the result that the skipper gave my father a thrashing because there was 'nae beef'.

Well do I remember the story of one of my father's chums who had torn his only pair o' breeks so often that there 'wis naething left t' hud the shewin''. As a last resort, his widowed mother shewed a square o' claith t' the heid-band o' the breeks an' jist lat the flap hing lowse! As you might expect, the ither loons wid creep up at his back to lift the flap and cry, 'Peep'! The peer loon wis a sittin' target for a byename, so they caaed him the Flapper. A few years later, the same Flapper stowed away to Canada, and did very well in the Hudson Bay Company. No doubt his spell with the flap had hardened him off for the Arctic.

Then there was the unforgettable day when a whaling-ship, homeward bound for Dundee, hailed a ripper-boatie off Buchan Ness. Would they take a message ashore? Aye! surely. Then the great ship's Captain handed my father, a loon in the boatie, a sum of money and a written message, with the request that he should go as soon as possible to the Post-office and send a telegram to the owners, to appraise them of the vessel's arrival on the morrow. A hale shillin'! And even after paying for the telegram there was a saxpence left! It wis a lang time afore he saw anither een.

Burnhaven had no proper harbour, so the Burnies had to draw their boats up on a stony beach, enlisting all the available women and bairns to help in the laborious task. Finally, however, it became obvious that the days of the small sailing-boats were over. Bigger, heavier boats were required, and you couldn't draw these up on a beach. There was even word of such things as steam-drifters that wouldn't need sails at all. Such craft would require to be kept afloat in a proper harbour, so the exodus to Peterhead began.

There must have been many a tear when it came to leaving the village with its earthen-floored cottages where they had reared their families, cottages whose floors had been regularly spread with clean sand, and just as regularly swept bare, ready for a fresh sanding. Of course, there had been the occasional 'fleer-o'-canvas', when the boat had required a new sail and the old one had been taken home to make a fine floor-covering. There, surely, is the origin of the term 'canvas', the fisher (and country) word for linoleum, still a thing of the future. There must have been hairts sair at leaving the little Congregational Chapel where they had worshipped so long; and yet it must have been a great adventure, especially for the youngsters, to whom Peterhead was a 'great muckle toon'.

Like most small fishing communities, Burnhaven had its 'characters', not all of whom lived to see the exodus, but whose profound sayings were handed down by oral tradition for many years, until finally they have been lost. Chief of these old personalities was Deevlick, a mixture of seer-cum-anointed-leear who made some remarkable predictions, some of which came to pass. His son, Deevlick's Willie, was a character in his own right. I knew him quite well when he lived in this town, a little mannie with phenomenal physical strength, and a forthright manner of speech liberally sprinkled with 'Foo? I'll tell ye foo'! He always addressed me as 'Cousin', and boys, he wis a bonny leear!

Now, entirely because of such characters, the Burnie race as a whole has been credited with the gift of mixing truth with fiction so skilfully that a boddy nivver kens far they are wi' them. They jist canna help it.

Is this then actually the case? That's a leading question; jist lat's say that some are better at it than ithers.

So, family by family the Burnies sattled in the Blue Toon. Those who came to the Burnie Streetie must have looked on their new homes as palaces. 'Fit? Twa storey hooses wi' widden fleers an' nae dubs at the door?'

But the Streetie couldna tak' them aa, so they spread far and wide through the toon, finding accommodation where they could. Some took to the Queenie, ithers to the Roanheids, while a goodly number settled in the Sooth Bey area, not very far from the present Life-boat shed.

The Burnies were in at the start of the steam-drifter era; forsaking the old ripper and smaa-line, they became remarkably good herring-and-great-line fishermen. Where a small tarred shed had sufficed for the storage of a few haddock lines, the Burnies now required more spacious accommodation for fleets of herring nets and huge baskets of heavy lines, to say nothing of the coils of tarry rope required by a herring fleet. Such heavy gear was kept in stores near the harbour, but the herring nets themselves were stored at home.

There now appeared on the scene a new breed of fisherman, the 'man wi' gear'. In the herring drifters, the 'clear baabees', that which was left after all expenses had been paid, was divided into three roughly equal parts, the boat's share, the nets' share and the crew's share. The boat's share of course went to the owners, of whom there could be quite a number, usually including the skipper. The nets' share went to those who owned the nets, usually the skippers and two or three crew members. Then there were the hired men, who got a share for their labour only. A great many hired men aspired to become men-wi'-gear, for, as a general rule, a man with a sixth of nets earned two shares, one for his labour and one for his nets. An owner/man-wi'-gear could do quite well, depending to a great extent on how big his share of nets was. Complicated? It was actually a sort of caste system, for when a fella became a man-wi'-gear he thought he was a cut above the hired man. And so he was, actually, in the pecking order. Hence the mythical tale that a certain life-boat crew, going alongside a drifter in distress, heard a self-important voice say, 'Men-wi'-gear first, noo, men-wi'-gear first'!

One old custom did the Burnies strictly observe. When a really close relative of the skipper died, the ship's white water-line was painted blue. A not-so-close relative merited only a blue 'mouth-piece' below the white at the fore end. When did you last see a blue water-line?

Noo, fit aboot the female o' the species? Weel, fin she got richt wa's t' paper, she papered them an' varnished the paper. Some o' the paper's still on the wa's, cos it's near impossible t' shift! Fin she got her new fleer o' canvas, she varnished that, an' fin she got a fine black grate wi' twa binks an' an oven, she black-leaded it, an' scoured the clear bits till they shone like silver. She became a first-class herring gutter and a top-notch net-mender, and she nivver had a holiday in her life.

For many years, after the fisher-folk left it, Burnhaven was a community of decent, hard-working country-folk and tradesmen, but gradually these people too moved on, in search of better things. The old fisher houses became roofless, weed-grown ruins, until at the end the remnants of the place were simply a haunt for squatters. Now there is not a single vestige remaining, and I fear it is verily possible that we'll lose even the very name.

Noo, fit aboot the Burnies' descendants? 'Fit? Twa storey hooses wi' widden fleers, an' nae dubs aboot the door?'

It is perfectly plain that, like the Children of Israel, they have come a long, long way from even that Mount Pisgah of progress.

But I'll tell ye ae thing! They're still the bonniest leears in Buchan, some better at it than ithers!

Can the Ethiopian change his skin, or the leopard his spots? Jeremiah 13-23.

The Haddock Rash

It was just last week, the first week of August, 1985, and I was admiring a bonny new boat moored about a hundred yards or so from my own front door. She was new and she was bonny at the same time, a combination somewhat rare in this modern world. To my mind, some of the latest vessels, and in particular a few of timber construction, are positively hideous. They are not merely broad in the beam; they are actually obese. They are not simply high-wooded; they are unnaturally lofty, and the result leaves me with a faint suspicion that somehow these boats were launched minus 25 or 30 feet of their length. Whatever the considerations that prescribed such dimensions, beauty was certainly not one of them; but then, maybe I'm old-fashioned.

But this was a bonny boat and an able boat all in one. A Lossie boat? Aye, surely! a study in black-and-white, all ready for sea.

'Let go!', cried the skipper, and I made for the mooring-rope; but I was forestalled by a swack young chiel on the foc'sle-head, or whaleback. Leaping lightly onto the quay, he drew from the hip pocket of his jeans a pair of bright orange plastic gloves which he swiftly donned before lowsin' the rope.

'Good grief', says I to myself. 'I've seen aathing noo.' Then I noticed that every visible crew-man was wearing gloves of various colours, and from that I gathered that this is standard practice, and rightly so. Hands which are doing rough work and handling heavy gear should be protected.

Then my thoughts went back in time to my own days at sea, when the use of gloves was unknown. Now, in the hauling of herring nets gloves were taboo, apart from the hauling of the cork-rope, where they were at times permissible. But for the men hauling the 'belly' (the sheet) of the net, bare hands were mandatory. Gloved hands simply tore the net to shreds, as did the unforgiveable practice of sticking one's fingers through the meshes. That simply resulted in lacerated fingers and badly holed nets. The secret was to get as much yarn as possible into your fist, keep the net square, and all haul together. Ragnails were common, but 'richt sair hands' were rare.

Seine-net fishing was a different kettle of fish, in more ways than one. Herring did not require to be gutted on board, whereas white fish had to be gutted, washed, and iced as soon as possible, especially if they were not to be landed for a few days, and now we meet the fisherman's deadly enemy, the 'Haddock Rash'. You've never heard of it? I'm not surprised.

You see, at a certain season of the year the haddocks were full of spawn, and in the gutting of these 'spawny haddocks' a mixture of spawn and slime would ooze between a fella's fingers, irritating the tender skin. Liberal dipping of the hands in water served to slow down the process slightly, but the end result was inevitably the 'haddock rash' which wasn't a rash at all, but simply the chafing of the skin between the fingers until the skin was non-existent. Now, THAT'S sair hands for ye. And to work day after day with such fingers was sheer hell. The trawlermen were the chief sufferers; they handled great bags of spawny haddocks, they were longer at sea, and they worked really inhuman hours.

Then there were the times when the haddocks 'took their ballast prior to a storm'. This was a false idea that some fishermen had; nevertheless there were times when the haddocks were full of slimy grit which had the same effect as spawn in that it removed the skin and left the 'prood flesh' atween the fingers. Oh, boys, that can be sair, sair. It's a poor, poor life when you must leave your front buttons undone because your fingers can neither fasten nor undo them.

And isn't it a gey sair fecht when, after three or four hours in your bunk you rise to face another twenty-hour day, only to find that your hands are half-shut as if smitten with arthritis, and will remain so until you have urinated on them? Filthy? Crude? Uncivilised? Maybe so, in the lily-white, sophisticated world of dry land, but the sea has never been and never will be a civilised environment. It has no time for prudery or squeamishness, and drastic pains need drastic remedies. Any trawlerman or seine-net-man of the old school will tell you the same, especially those who never knew what it was to wear gloves.

Now, what about our noble brethren, the line men? How did they fare? Theirs was a completely different trade; no tremendous bags of small fish for them. No! They took their great fish on board one by one, dragging them up from dark depths on strong hard lines so tightly laid that they resembled wire.

Now, although its name means 'heavy line', the great-line is not thick enough to afford the human hand a proper grip, so the strain, terrific at times, really falls where the fingers meet the palm of the hand. Hour after hour, day after day of such unnatural strain is bound to take its toll, and the hands become 'aa grippit', resembling arthritic claws. Same affliction as the trawlermen; same temporary early morning treatment; sair, sair hands. The line man's only protection was 'gags' or 'gyaags', circlets of flannel about two inches wide, worn round the hands to improve the grip when the strain was excessive. Then there were the stobs from the great muckle heuks, usually rusty, and the scratches from the teeth of the great fish as they were 'heukit' (taken off the hook). Septic sores are the bane of the line-man's life. 'Beelin's an' poultices, sair, sair hands awyte.'

The sma'-line men had their own problems. Since their gear was so much lighter, they had less strain on their hands, but sma'-line heuks are exceedingly sharp, and lug-worm bait is notoriously poisonous. So the sma'-boat lads got their fair share o' 'futtlie beelin's'.

But sma' lines were not always worked from sma' boats. There was a time when drifters from the East coast went sma'-line fishing around Whiten Head and Loch Eriboll, and also in the Minch. A fine canny jobbie, think ye? It was sheer, murderous slavery. Shoot and haul 20 nets for herring bait; cut the herring into thousands of baits; bait and shoot the lines; sleep for two hours (the two watch-keepers would get only one hour apiece); haul the lines and stow away the gutted catch; redd the lines, making good any 'wants' (missing hooks); shoot and haul the nets again; and so on. I am quite certain that any farmer working his horses in such a fashion would have gone to prison, and rightly so. But alas, there are times when human beings count for less than the beasts of the field.

I have a friend in the Broch who could tell you a harrowing story how, one night when his fingers were literally to the bone, the skipper took pity on him and baited his line for him, not because the bones of the poor lad's fingers were actually visible, but simply because the line was being baited too slowly. The poor sufferer was given a different jobbie instead. Belsen, did ye say? A week at that, and ye'll be like a Zombie!

I've forgotten to tell ye that, shortly after the Hitler war, the fishers tried using cotton industrial gloves, but they were not a success. The seams on the insides of the fingers were themselves a serious irritant, and even when they were 'flypit', the cotton absorbed the irritants from the fish and transmitted them to the fingers so we were back to square one. Then plastic gloves made their appearance, but these were so stiff and unyielding that they were almost useless.

Over the years, however, the boffins have developed plastic gloves which are seamless, waterproof and really pliable, 'jist the verra dunt'.

But have we not overlooked one class of fisher? Fit aboot the ripper men? The ripper is a primitive yet effective method of catching codlings without bait. It has been called 'the poor man's friend' or 'the murderer'. It has also been described as 'a lump o' leed at ae end, an' a feel at the ither'. I prefer to call it 'the Alpha and Omega', the beginning and the end. How many fishermen have started out as mere boys, 'oot for a go at the ripper in a sma' boatie wi' an aul' mannie'? And how swiftly do the years come full circle so that, in the end, they themselves are the 'aul mannie'? Alpha and Omega are never far apart.

Now it happens that I'm an aul' mannie in a sma' boatie tryin' t' catch a puckly codlin's t' saut an' dry for hard fish t' mak' 'hairy tatties'. I've discovered that plastic gloves fairly save a boddy's hands fae the chafe o' the ripper string (line). But, boys, they're aafa dear! I ken the young fishermen buy them by the bundle, but the likes o' me could nivver look at that. Oor tattie man says we'll be lucky t' get mait this winter, an' I'm thinkin' he's richt. Still, I shouldna compleen ower muckle; ye see, I'm gettin' my gloves free noo!

'An' far wid ye get that?', says you. 'In the hairber!', says I. 'Fifty or sixty pair ony mornin' ye like. Aa sizes an' colours, floatin', grisly like wi' their fingers to the sky, an' nine times oot o' ten there's nae a thing wrang wi' them. Oh, sic a prodigal, wasteful generation! Fancy aa that siller floatin' aboot like caff!'

But I'd better nae say ower muckle aboot that, either. Ye see, if the young lads wis t' stop bein' careless, I'd hae t' buy gloves, an' that jist widna dee ava.

Keep the glovies comin', lads, keep them comin'. Jist mine fit the Lord said, lang, lang ago – 'The poor ye have always with you'.

But, if ye're nae ower happy wi' that sayin', ye could aye try 'The Jews is nae aa in Jerusalem'!

Finally, brethren, let me tell you something else. I'm fine acquaint wi' a chiel that keeps his boatie aside mine, but he disna pick up ony gloves. No; he picks up lemonade bottles! Fancy that now! Aye, and from the sale of these bottles several charities have in turn benefited to the tune of several hundreds of pounds. Now, that's MAGIC!

Black and White

On any steam drifter the capstan was an indispensible unit of power. Always sited on the fore-deck, slightly to starboard of midships, it was driven by a sturdy little steam engine (twin-cylinder) on its top storey. A system of cog-and-pinion gearing drove the great vertical barrel which took the heavy, tarred bush-rope during the hauling process. Simply by removing a small cog-wheel, one could dispense with the big barrel and drive instead a small horizontal pulley which was used for hoisting out the catch. If ever there was a boon to fishermen, it was the steam capstan, so rugged and reliable that it was often neglected.

Behold now, Duncan, the Turk's driver busy at the *Meadowsweet's* capstan as she lay tied to the quay in her home port. Duncan, conscientious sowl, was checking and lubricating the intimmers o' the machine, while close-by the Turk and his deck squad were seated on fish-boxes, busily mending holes in the nets, holes which had been 'laid ower' for attention. It was really amazing how such seemingly clumsy fingers could be so adroit with a mending needle.

The proximity of sailing-time was evident from the steadily thickening pall of smoke from the countless funnels, a pall sometimes dense enough to shut out the very sunlight itself.

'I can hear somebody singin' hymns somewye', says Duncan. 'Fa on earth can that be, at this time o' day?'

'Faith Mission Pilgrims fae Ireland, I wid think', says the Turk. 'They come here ilkie summer. I like t' hear them singin'.'

'Ye're a queer lot, you fisher folk', says Duncan, wi' a lach. 'Ye hiv aboot five-an'-twenty different sects in the toon already, an' still ye're nae pleased. Ye surely dinna need a puckle Irishmen t' come here an' preach!'

'Ye're richt aboot the sects, Duncan, but the Irish come here o' their ain free will, nae because we need them. Mysel', I wid hae aabody aneth ae reef, but them that's aneth ae reef already, dinna aye sowder ower weel, so I'm thinkin' that t' pit the hale jing-bang thegither wid be jist like a hawker's rebellion. There's mair than ae sect aboord here, freen, so ye'd better let that flee stick t' the wa'.'

'Hiz country folk's nae bothered wi' that cairry-on ava. Ye see, skipper, we hiv jist the wan Kirk, an' that dis fine wi aabody.'

'Gran'!' says the Turk, 'Jist gran'. Noo, if there's jist the ae Kirk, she'll be rale full on a Sunday mornin'. Ye wid need t' be awa early t' get a seat?'

Duncan had no answer to such a body blow.

'Aye-aye, Duncan, fan wis ye last in the kirk?'

'Christmas, skipper.'

'An' fan are ye gaun back, Duncan?'

'Christmas, skipper! Ye see, I wis christened in the kirk, I wid like t' be mairried in the kirk, an' if I'm spared an' weel, I'd like t' be buried oot o' the kirk!'

'Weel, ye micht manage that! If ye're spared an' weel! Noo, seein' that ye're deen wi' the caipsan, stand by at yer engine. We'll awa oot wi' the lave.'

The steam drifter could not be handled by remote control; there had to be someone in the engine-room to activate the massive engine as the skipper might require. All signals from the skipper to the chief were transmitted by means of a clanging telegraph. When the vessel had cleared the breakwaters, the skipper would signal 'All Clear' so the chief could come up for a breather if he so wished.

Thus, an hour or so later, we find Duncan in the wheel-house with the Turk.

'Fit like, skipper?' says he. 'I hope ye didna think naething fin I said that you fisher folk wis queer. I've come t' like the fishers, an' they're nae aa queer; jist a puckly o' them. I think the queerest eens is them that says they're Christians. Fit div ye think, skipper?'

'There's naething so queer as folk, Duncan, whether they be Christians or Frinch-Canadian Jews.'

Duncan could see that the Turk would not willingly commit himself, so he tried a fresh approach.

'We hiv some gey queer folk in the country places tee, skipper!'

'I'm listenin', Duncan.'

'Weel, we hiv a lad up aside hiz at Povertyknap, an' he says he's a Christian, but I dinna think there's a Christian hair in his heid. Oh, he's awa t' the Kirk ilkie Sunday mornin', him an' his wife, wi' the horse an' gig. But I think there's mair than that till't. Fit div ee think, skipper?'

'I'm listenin', Duncan, I'm listenin'.'

'Weel,' continued Duncan. 'This kirk-greedy fairmer's caa'ed Baldy, an' he has the twa biggest an' best fairms in Buchan, I wid say. Aathing grows for Baldy, better than for ither folk, an' his kye's aye wydin' up t' the udders amon' girss. Gran' kye they are tee, an' I'm sure he has hunners o' them! Black-an-fite, ivvery wan o' them. Div ye ken onything aboot coos, skipper?'

'Coos?' says the Turk. 'Coos is yon beasts that ye see in the parks. Yon craiters that we get oor milk fae. They tell me that they're nae aa coos; jist them that has the bagpipes aneth them. Is that richt, Duncan?'

'It's easy seen that ye're fisher, you an' yer bagpipes, but ye're richt,' laughed Duncan. 'Noo, iss is fit I wis gaun t' tell ye. Atween Povertyknap an' Baldy's place there's a little wee placie that's hardly worth a name; jist a sklyter o' roch grun, as Flora Garry says. Gweed kens fit wye the faimly that bides on't gets a livin'. It maun be gey han'-t'-mou! Sandy, the man himsel' disna keep weel ava; something t' dee wi' bein' gassed in the trenches, I think. There's a gey puckle days he keeps the loon fae the skweel; in fact he's been in trouble for that, but little difference dis't mak'. I doot if Sandy could mak' a livin' yonner supposin' he wis weel. But, mind ye, he's a dour, thrawn, contermashious sod, the same Sandy; he jist winna tak' help fae naebody ava. Mony a time has my ain folk offered t' help, an' so has Baldy, but Sandy says he'll manage fine himsel', even fin he's fair stuck.'

'There's folk like that amon' the fisher folk, ana, Duncan,' says the Turk.

'I'm nae neen surprised at that! Div ye ken onything aboot coos gaun dry?'

'Me? No! I dinna ken naething aboot that, Duncan; I'm fisher, ye ken!'

'Weel,' continued Duncan, 'Ivvery coo gings dry noo an' again; it's a mercy they dinna aa ging dry at the same

Part of the fleet in the mid twenties. In the background, two famous, vanished landmarks – The Gut-factory Lum and the Black Shed.

*Roughly one twentieth of the fleet as they enter Yarmouth. In the lead, a B.F. Zulu, an M.L. Fifie (*White Heather*), both motorised; and the P.D. steam drifter* Twinkling Star. *Say 1929.*

time, cos fin a coo gings dry, she has nae milk. An' that's jist fit happened t' Sandy's coo at a time fin Sandy wis richt nae-weel.'

'Dis Sandy nae hae anither coo?', says the Turk, surprised. 'I thocht he wid surely hae mair than een!'

'Nivver!' says Duncan, 'Yon placie wid be gey sair made t' support anither beast. Onywye, it wis pure disaster for Sandy's faimly; nae milk, nae butter, nae cheese, an' precious fyowe maiks aboot the place forbye. Aabody wis winnerin' fit wid happen noo, wi' Sandy bein' the kind o' chiel he is, ye see, fin the bold Baldy tak's the bull b' the horns, an' fit dis he dee, think ye?'

'I'm listenin', Duncan!', says the Turk.

'Weel, skipper, he gings doon t' see Sandy as if he didna ken the man wis badly, an' he says 'I'm sorry t' see ye're laid-up, Sandy, cos I'm doon t' seek an obligement fae ye'!

'Fae me!'? says Sandy, 'Fit wye could the likes o' me oblige the likes o' you?'

'Weel, Sandy, I've a problem! Yon loons o' mine lat me doon, fyles, an' there's been a miscoont, so I've twa coos that I jist hinna room for. I'm winnerin' if ee wid be willin' t' tak' them an' look aifter them for a fylie till I get things sorted oot. T'wid be a great help t' me!'

Sandy lies a fylie thinkin', syne he looks up an' says, 'I'd be mair than willin' t' help ye oot, but ye ken this place couldna feed three beasts'.

'Och, that's nae bother ava, Sandy. I'll see till't that yon loons o' mine tak's ower plinty o' mait.'

'Aa richt, than,' says Sandy, an' they shook han's on that.

'Hey!', says the Turk, 'Faa wid get aa the milk?'

'Oh, Sandy wid get the milk; that's the laa up the country, tho' I dinna think it's written doon.'

'Noo, Duncan, fit gars ye think that Baldy's nae a Christian? Mysel', I'm thinkin' he's jist a Topper.'

'Weel, skipper,' says Duncan, 'Baldy tellt Sandy a damt great lee! He said he hidna room for the twa coos. Od, aabody kens that wis a lee. He had room for a lot mair than that. Christians shouldna tell lees ava, should they, skipper?'

The Turk was silent for a fylie, then he said, quaet like, 'Duncan, my loon, fit kine o' coos did Baldy gie Sandy. Black-an'-fite?'

'That's richt, skipper, black-an'-fite. The twa best milkers in Buchan!'

'Weel,' says the Turk, 'I'm thinkin' Baldy jist tellt a black-an'-fite lee, an' I'm sure that kine disna coont.'

'Ach!', says Duncan, 'I'm awa below t' gie her a shiffle o' coal. Ye're a richt queer lot, you fishers!'

Oral Tradition

I have never liked History and by History I mean the stuff we got at school. Ye ken, Kings and Queens and Battles and the Dates thereof. This was a subject which gave my tiny mind a few insurmountable problems, for I simply couldn't remember dates. To this very day, I have the same failing; birthdays and anniversaries don't seem to register and, were I not gently reminded, no one would ever get a present or a card for their birthday.

In one respect I am rather fortunate, for my wedding anniversary falls on the 26th of January, and I would be thick indeed if I missed that, seeing that Robbie Burns' birthday is on the 25th. As soon as I hear somebody singing 'There wis a lad wis born in Kyle' I'm reminded that 'She'll be lookin' for a bunchie o' flooers the morn, an' flooers is an aafa price at this time o' year'!

There was one memorable occasion when I really did excel myself in the historic field. Teacher had set us the task of writing an essay on the Battle of Bannockburn and, since essays had never given me any trouble, I set to with a will. I would show them that I knew my history better than they gave me credit for. Boys, I was proud of that essay, my sole attempt at an historic novel for, in glowing style and in graphic detail, I described how Wallace the Bruce, on a Shetland pony, stood in his stirrups and, with one fell swipe of his battle-axe severed John o' Groats' head from his shoulders as he thundered past on his war-horse. The marks I got for that glowing effort caused me to give up History as a dead loss.

Oral tradition, now, is an entirely different kettle o' fish, one of whose attractions is its delightful vagueness – there are never any dates. These old tales, handed down from generation to generation, have a tendency to lose the names of the principal characters, possibly conveniently, but they suffer little on that account. And, furthermore, the age-old stories deal with common, ordinary folk like you and me. Surely that's better material than Kings and Queens and Courtiers in all their finery and lace. I can assure you that there's no lace in the tale which I'd like to tell you now, just as I heard it, via oral tradition. In fact, there are two tales, neither of which is to be found in any History book.

Once upon a time, then, and not so very long ago at that, in one of the three fisher villages which lie between the Broch and Rattray Head, there were two brothers who had fished together for several years. They must have been reasonably successful, for they were having a new boat built. Say, about 30ft in length. All was well until the boat was completed and ready for launching; then, for some unknown reason the brothers 'keest oot'. For a considerable time the boat was left on the stocks, pending some sort of agreement between the two owners, but neither brother would yield. Finally it was decided that they would 'get the shaavie' ('shaav' being the local term for a saw). So the boat was actually sawn into two halves, and each brother was left to arrange for the transporting of his own particular half to his own particular home. There, each half was turned bottom up and set on a low dykie built to receive it, so, instead of one bonny boat, the brothers had two peculiar sheds!

'Ah,' you may say, 'This is only some sort of parable to demonstrate the bitterness which can creep into quarrels between brothers. It cannot possibly be true.'

But, all too sadly, it IS true, and for many a long day did the two half-boats grace the village scene. To the best of my knowledge there is no written record of this event, but oral tradition has kept it from being utterly lost.

Now, what about the four sail-boaties that left Cairnbulg long, long ago, making for Neebra Watter (the Ythan Estuary), to collect mussel bait for their haddock lines? This was common practice, for it was by far the best method of acquiring an ample stock of bait. They could simply help themselves, and there would be no transport fees. With a favouring wind and a flood tide the flotilla reached their destination without incident. On the ebbing tide the boats were beached among the rich mussel beds, and at low water the crews simply shovelled mussels into the open hulls, knowing that the incoming tide would refloat the boats. Steam puffers on the Tay regularly followed a similar practice. When a load of sand was required for some project, the puffer was grounded on a sandbank; then, when the tide receded, the crew shovelled sand into great iron buckets which were heaved on board by means of winch and derrick, to be tipped into the hold. Then the rising tide would refloat the laden vessel.

It is probable that the fishermen, in an excess of zeal, overloaded their boats. You know how it is. – 'Och! She'll hud a puckly mair yet. Eence we're here, we micht as well tak' them'. As it happened, that was a great mistake, for when the boaties sailed for home, probably next morning, they were in no fit state to meet bad weather. There was very little wind as they crossed the bar but, against the flood tide, their northward progress was painfully slow. By the time they had reached the Scaurs o' Cruden, the wind had backed to the south-east and was freshening slowly. An hour or so later there was really too much weather for heavily laden, undecked open boats. Not a storm, by any means, but still too much.

One boat foundered with the loss of all hands; the others were very fortunate indeed to reach the safety of Peterhead which, in the days before the breakwaters were built, was a very dicey entrance indeed. The three boats completed their passage a day or two later.

As one would expect, there was a deep sense of shock throughout the fisher community; there were the usual manifestations of grief, widow's blacks and memorial services for young men sadly missed. Indeed, for several weeks, there was an almost tangible air of gloom about the village. Then everything seemed to change.

Someone with a malicious tongue and a wicked heart sowed the seeds of doubt and suspicion. There were dark whisperings at gable ends, there were little knots of gossiping women who melted into handy doorways at the approach of certain men. There was an unwonted averting of the gaze as friend met former friend, and certain bairns were forbidden to play with certain other bairns. Distrust walked the village lanes like a spectre, until the festering sore finally burst open when ae loon said till anither loon, 'Your father droont my father! My father wis in the sea, hingin' on till an oar, an' your father sailed his boat that close that he chappit my father's verra fingers. But he didna lift a finger t' save him'!

So the dark secret was out! Bairns say what they hear their elders say, but they don't always say it in secret. According to rumour, three crews had sailed on, leaving another crew to perish in the deep!

I cannot accept that! I do believe that, on the sad day in question, it was a fight for survival, and if succour could have been given, it would have been forthcoming. But, having said that, I am perfectly willing to accept the tale when it deals with the whispered innuendoes and their dire results. There's naething so queer as folk, and fisher folk can be as queer and coorse and ill-thochtit as any.

Thus it came to pass that three crews, finding life in their native place completely intolerable, set sail there-from, again on a southerly course. The setting sun saw them draw their boats up on the sandy beach at the mouth of the Cruden Burn, where there was no harbour, and the stars looked down to see them asleep beneath an upturned boat. In such a fashion did the first fishers come to that haven known as the Ward.

From the following dawn they had a sair, sair fecht. It was a case of starting from scratch, and that is never easy. Just as they had done at home, the strangers followed their calling, bartering their fish among the country folk. Only at the Castle on the cliff was there a cash customer, a customer who showed a deep interest in their welfare, sending them an occasional boll of meal to help them along. In rough-and-ready wooden shacks built by them-selves on the sand dunes, the fishers dwelt with their wives and bairns who had followed them south, probably on foot. And thus they formed a small, close-knit community, known to the locals as the Binties, the folk that lived on the bints, or sand dunes.

It is more than likely that the Laird, in his cliff-top castle, knew the reason for the sudden appearance of the strangers. Even in those distant days, Lairds would have had means of communicating with each other. In any case, this particular Laird kept the incomers under close observation, taking due note that they were an eident, sober and honest lot. In due course the good man had compassion on the Binties, living as they were in such awful conditions, and built houses for them on the North side of the burn. So the Binties crossed over to the other side and became Wardies, merging into the local scene as to the manner born.

At a much later date a wealthy shipping magnate built for them a harbour whose piers would have been much stronger if more of the local granite had been used in their construction. Still, the piers served the fishers very well for many a long year. Indeed, they served until there were no fishers to use them. Nowadays the harbour is simply a haven for pleasure craft, a place beloved by Sunday visitors.

But although the fishers have long since departed, their names remain. Tait, Summers and Duthie take their place alongside local names such as Robertson, Masson and Milne, but the first three of these names were brought to the Ward by the Binties who, in the words of one of their leaders were 'A cursed tribe, driven from home'.

'Och!', says you, 'They're nae a hunner mile awa fae their folk that bides on the north side o' Rattray Heid. Are ye sure that they ARE the same folk?'

Aye surely! They're the same folk aa richt, an' they're nae aa that far apairt. Jist as far as a boatie could reason-ably sail in a day.

Now, THAT'S oral tradition, the stuff ye dinna get in History books.

But then, as I've said, I've nivver likit History!

The Fite Rubbit

It was in the mid thirties that the great change took place. Somebody had produced a new green preservative to replace the bark which generations of fishermen had used on their herring nets. The new preservative was to be the final blow in the war against rot in natural fibres; at least, that was the claim. But the herring men wouldn't look at the stuff, and for at least another 25 years they stuck to the old-fashioned ways, until nylon herring nets made their appearance. Great stuff, nylon! No more rotten nets! But nylon nets were very expensive, so it was only a gradual phase-out of the old-style cotton nets that could be contemplated. Then, before nylon had time to make any real impact, the bottom fell out of the herring trade, and countless thousands of herring nets were sold off for garden netting.

The trawlermen too, looked askance at the new green stuff (a derivative of copper), and for a long time they continued to use the traditional tarred manilla trawls. Indeed, there was very little change in the trawlers until the post-war appearance of man-made fibres which came in all the colours of the rainbow, the most common shade being bright orange, and the material Courlene.

So, in the beginning it was left to the seine-net men to try out the bright green stuffie, and we were among the first, if not the very first in Peterhead to try it. In those days we rigged our own nets; i.e. we bought the treated netting from the factory, sewed the pieces together, then mounted the net on its ropes to our own specifications, thus saving quite a bit of cash. Those were the days when we used flat ovals of cork as floats, or even herring corks, but we detested the green glass balls which the trawlers used; they were much too easily broken. Metal floats were in their early infancy, and plastic floats were 25/30 years in the future. What was plastic, anyhow?

Well, now, to get on with the tale! We rigged a bonny new green net with raips, corks and lead weights, but in the process we noticed that the green stuffie was not quite dry; so we asked the net-factory for advice.

'Not to worry', they said. 'But it would do no harm to let the net hang in the fresh air for a week or so;' and this we did.

At three o'clock in the morning of the following Monday the three of us met at the boat, ready to go to sea. The three comprised my elder brother, John, who was the skipper, brother-in-law Charlie and myself.

C'mon' says John. 'We'll tak the new net aff the dyke, an' see hoo she fishes.' So we made for the dyke at the back o' the market, but, as we neared the net, John says.

'Leave the net far she is. We'll dee athoot 'er for a day.'

'Fit's adee? Is there something wrang?' says I.

'Aye!' says he, 'Div ye nae see fit's sittin' on the net?'

'Fine that!' says I, 'It's a cat!'

'Aye, it's a cat,' says he, 'But it's a fite cat, so jist leave the net far she is. A fite cat wis nivver gweed.'

'Och!', says I. 'We're in the twentieth century, an' we're bothered aboot the colour o' a cat! The cat could be tartan, for me! Hish! I thocht that kind o' stuff wis deid lang ago; I've heard o' fite elephants, but fite cats? Nivver!'

'Aa richt! Aa richt!, says John, 'We'll tak the net aboard, but jist mine fit I tellt ye!'

Well, now, we shot the bonny net, but we never saw her again. We lost her in a heap of sunken wreckage and, of course, the fite cat got the blame. Me? I blamed the skipper for nae wytin' a wee fylie till the sky wis licht eneuch for us to see oor landmarks.

Still, boys, it WIS a fite cat!

Now let us jump forward, say a full twenty years. Brother John had been obliged to quit the sea for health reasons, and now I was in command of the *Twinkling Star* PD137, a 56 footer built by Geordie Forbes on the Queenie. We were fishing most days near the out-edge of the Buchan Deep, the bulk of our catch being whitings which were consigned nightly by lorry from Peterhead to Aberdeen fish-market, for at that time Peterhead as a market was defunct. With whiting at twenty-three shillings (£1.15) a box, it was a sair fecht to get a living.

I was one of a generation whose motto was 'If ye canna pey for something, then ye jist dee athoot it'. A strange motto in today's world, I'm sure. But, when you consider today's world of inflation and high prices, it's difficult to see how young folk can possibly get a start at all without some kind of 'never-never' system. I mention this in passing because, after years of aiming for it, I had got myself a car, a birch-grey Morris 1000, and suddenly a whole new world opened up. Places which heretofore had been mere names on a map became realities within easy reach. Deeside and Tomintoul, the Moray Firth ports and West-coast villages became part of Life, and what a transformation that was! After a week of looking at the sea, I could go and feast my gaze on beauty.

Well, now, to get on with the tale. We had spent a glorious day in the country, one of those halcyon days when fisher-folk make for the hills, and country-folk make for the beaches. Far and wide had we ranged, and now, as evening drew nigh we were making our leisurely way homewards. Through Foggie and Turra we came, the wife, the bairn and myself, when suddenly, nae far fae the Brunt Smiddy we saw, at the roadside a little quinie greetin' – jist brakkin' her hairt!

'Fit's adee, my quine?' says I, stopping the car.

'Oh,' says she. 'I've lost my rubbitie, an' I'll nivver get it back!'

'Fit gars ye think 'at?', says I. 'It canna be jist hine awa, surely.'

'Oh,' she says, 'It's geen in amon' 'at stuff ower air!'

Now, ''at stuff ower air' was a wilderness if ever I saw one. There wis thistles an' nettles an' brammles an' whins an' aa mortal thing that a fisher chiel should bide clear o'. But in my ignorance I saw no dangers; I saw only a damsel in distress and a golden opportunity for me to be a knight in shining armour. (In other words, a great feel.)

'Dinna greet, my quine,' says I. 'I'll seen get yer rubbitie!' An' in I goes like a warrior.

Boys, oh boys, I got the rubbitie a'richt, but oh, siccan a sotter I wis in afore I got oot again! I wis scartit an' torn, same as tho' I'd been trailed backlins throwe a hedge. If I'd been a proper knight, I wid ha' heen armour on, but nae me! Sensible to the last, an' died ravin'!

Oor bairn (she has a bairnie o' her ain, noo), mines fine on that nicht, cos the bonny fite beastie wi' the pink e'en scartit her fin she cuddled it. Then the battle-scarred warrior got into his car and made for hame, his scarts an'

stobs nippin' like murder. Still, Saiterday hadna been wasted; he had left somebody happy.

Now, let's jump ahead to the early hours of Monday morning. The PD seiners are on their first haul of the long, long summer day, and, since there are as yet no fish to handle, the crews (apart from the men at the winch) are relatively inactive, and the skippers are newsin' aboot this an' that on the ship-to-ship radio. Maistly claik, ye ken, but eence they start gettin' fish it's a different Muggie Rennie, for then the same skippers turn into the biggest leears ye're ever likely to meet. I'm tellin' ye, the skipper that tells his brother skipper the truth is a rare bird indeed, – something like the Dodo.

But this was the first haul of the week, and there wis nae lees. (Yet).

'Fit like Peter?', says Willie Reid of the *Traveller*. 'Did ye hae a fine week-end? Far wis ye, an' fit aboot it? C'mon an' gie's yer news.

'Oh, Bill,' says I, 'We had a rare experience on Saiterday nicht. I got inveigled wi' a fite rubbitie, an' ye nivver saw sic a maneer aa yer days.'

Then I launched into the tale aboot the bonny fite beastie, nae forgettin' to tell him jist hoo brave I'd been in the jungle. If Bill wis ony man ava, he wid spik to Patrick Wolrige-Gordon MP so that I wid get a medal.

When I had finished my yarn, there was a long, deep silence before Bill replied.

'I'm amazed that a man o' your intelligence an' experience should mention sic a beastie on a Monday mornin'. An' specially a fite een. Eh, wah-wah!'

'Now, Bill,' says I, 'I'm amazed at you thinkin' there's onything in the aul superstitions. I've nae time for them mysel'; they're jist a lot o' guff!'

'Tell me that fin the day's deen!' says he.

He was referring, of course, to the old belief that to use certain words was simply to invite disaster. The actual names of a few animals were taboo, and a substitute name must be used if mention of the creature was unavoidable. Thus a rabbit became a 'fower-fitter' or a 'mappie', depending on your port of origin. The pig became a 'grunter' or a 'Sandy Campbell/Sonnie Cammle'; the salmon became a 'reid fish' or simply 'caul' iron'. Ministers of the Gospel were not welcome near the boats, and should always be called 'sky-pilots'.

All these heathenish customs amused me greatly, and for the life of me I simply could not see how the use of the word 'rubbit' could have any effect on a day's fishing. That was utterly ridiculous!

Well, now, three times that day we had a 'foul bag', the net being so twisted that it couldn't fish; twice we broke a perfectly good rope, and once we got stuck in a 'fastener' on the sea-bed where we never 'came fast' before nor since. We should have gone home at dinner-time, but I was determined to prove a point. I didn't.

That was one awful day, the only day in all my time at sea that we put in a full day's work without having one single fish to land!

So how does this affect my attitude to superstition?

Well, lat me pit it this wye. Next time I see a quinie at the roadside greetin' for her fite rubbitie, she can bloomin'-well greet!

The Jacket

Simply because his name was Sandy Penny, the fisher loons called him Copper. He was as country as a peat, for his father had a placie near Longside, and that made Copper more or less a foreigner. Six mile inland? Very few of us fishers had ever been as far as that from the sea! (Sunday School picnics excepted, of course.)

Nevertheless, Copper had close links with Peterhead, for his mother was a Bluemogganer by the name of Bella Watson, whose mother had a shoppie in the Kirktoon. How Copper loved to spend his school holidays 'bidin' wi's Grunny', for to him the Blue Toon was a great metropolis, a hive of activity where horses by the score dragged all shapes and sizes of carts. There were even motor lorries with solid rubber tyres, and, believe it or not, there were at least six motor cars. Boys! What a steer! This was some Toon!

And then there was the Harbour, choc-a-bloc with boats, and Copper simply delighted in boats. Length and beam meant nothing to him. There were no drifters, liners, trawlers or seiners in Copper's world, – just boats. He drew no distinction between ripper yoles and cargo ships; they were all boats, and they all sailed on 'the watter', the country word for 'the sea'.

Yet, despite his rural background, Copper was a remarkably fine playmate. He ran barfit like the lave o's, and soon learned how to tie a hook on a line, how to take a fish off the hook, and how to carry as many as sixteen herring on his fingers when there was no string handy.

Many a bonny fry did he scran for his Grunny, though I suspect most of the fish found their way to the placie near Longside.

Copper and I became close friends. I was his confidant, as he was mine, and many were the boyhood dreams we shared. I shall never forget the bonny summer evening when the two of us sat on the 'tumble-home' stern of an old wooden drifter berthed in Port Henry. We were busy fishing for conger eels which abounded in the clear waters near the old, derelict hulls. We never actually caught any, and I think we were both secretly relieved, for I'm sure we were both just as secretly scared of the long, dark shapes that slunk around the rudders and propellers of the old ships. As we sat there in carefree fellowship, Copper suddenly turned to me and said, in his aul-farrant tongue, 'Od! I wid fairly like t' hae a boat o' my ain, someday!'

'Foo big a boat, Copper?', says I, surprised.

'Och! Nae a great muckle boat! Say, the size o' that een there!'

The boat in question was about thirty feet, just a big ripper yole.

Now, not even I, a fisher loon had got around to thinking as far ahead as that. Copper wi' a boat o's ain? Nivver! But not for all the tea in China would I hurt his feelings by telling him that his was an impossible dream. Country folk jist didna hae boats.

Came the time for leaving school, and thereafter I saw very little of Copper. He was the loon on his father's fairm, and I was the loon on my father's boat, so our paths lay far apart. The only real link between us was the shoppie in the Kirktoon where Copper's Grunny sellt sowens, that bitter brew made by the fermenting of corn husks or 'sids' in water for several days. That same brew, when brought to the boil in a pan and liberally sweetened with syrup, produced a sort of thick soup or pottage greatly relished by the old folks, especially at bedtime. On my occasional calls at the shoppie for a flagon of sowens for my mother, I always got a full report of Copper's progress.

During the War years, Copper and I never met at all but, in the first summer thereafter, who should come on board our boat but Copper himself, 'Sair needin' a fry o' herrin'.' It must have been shortly after Aikey Fair, for he had with him a puckle early tatties. Oh, he got his fry, sure enough, but not on his fingers this time. His basketie was filled and he went home delighted.

From that day our old friendship was renewed. With our wives and families, we would visit each other, and there was a regular swopping of fish for farm produce. There was never any question of cash, nor was there any question of either one of us being in the other's debt. 'It's nae loss fit a freen gets', and it worked very well indeed for many years.

Then came the day when Copper informed me rather proudly that he had 'gotten a place o' his ain, a hunner an' thirty acre arable an' a great skelp o' roch grun', in the Parish o' St Fergus, nae far fae the sea!'

'That's fine!' says I. 'Jist gran'. But fit aboot the boat ye wis gaan t' get? Nae sign o' her yet?'

He just laughed and shook his head. 'Gimme time, man. Gimme time.' Mrs Copper had never heard of the boat, and now that she did hear, she gave her man a long, hard look and said very drily, 'Aye! That'll be the day! Ye've plinty on yer plate, athoot a boat'.

Imagine my surprise, then, when Copper came to me some six months later in a state of great excitement. 'Ye'll nivver believe this!' says he, 'but I've gotten a boat!'

'Oh aye!', says I, in disbelief. 'Foo big a boat, freen'?'

'Aboot thirty fitt, or maybe a hackie mair. I'd like ye t' come an' hae a look at her.'

'Surely!' says I. 'Far is she?'

'She's in the san' at Scotston Heid. Nae far fae the fairm.'

'Ye mean she's ON the san', Copper. Divn't ye?'

'Na!' says he. 'She's IN the san'. Mair or less buried in't!'

It transpired that Copper had gone to the beach with his tractor and bogie for a load of sand and, since he was Copper, he would need to 'hae a look at the watter'. He could scarcely believe his eyes when he saw the starboard rail of a boat protruding from the sand. All of her port side, and most of her deck were still hidden, but there was little doubt that a complete hull lay there.

When I saw the boat, I realised that she had been cast ashore in the terrible North-east storm of the previous year, when three similar boats had disappeared with all hands. In spite of an appallingly low glass and a fearsome forecast, some of the inshore fleet had gone to sea in calm weather. Well, they wouldn't be far from the shore, and they would manage to make port before things became too bad. There would be the normal breathing space, of course, but, in fact disaster had overtaken them, for the tempest had leapt upon them with the sudden ferocity and power which is nowadays classed as the 'Once in a hundred years' storm. The boaties simply had no chance. Very few of them had survived, and the boat which lay before us was one of the hapless victims.

Now the cruel sea, with one of the biggest tides of the year, was slowly but surely removing the great bank of sand and tangles which had covered the wreck whose precise identity was unknown. Only a few scraps remained of the bulwark planking which had borne her name and registration numbers. So she was simply one of three identical missing hulls. Not even the paint could provide a clue, for each hull had been painted alike.

'I've seen the Receiver of Wrecks and the Insurance folk', says Copper. 'But they're jist nae interested! They say I should burn her for firewood!'

'I wid say the same,' says I. 'In fact I wid burn her far she lies!'

But Copper simply would not listen. 'I'll mak' a boat oot o' her! She's mine!'

'Weel, weel!', says I, seeing his obstinacy. 'Ye'll need t' get the san' oot o' the boat first, then get the boat oot o' the san', an' that'll be a gey sair fecht. She's as full o' san' as an egg's full o' mait!'

But, undismayed, Copper and his two sons tackled the

job of removing the sand from the boat's interior. It was slow, laborious work, for they had to work from a steeply sloping deck, and the hatchway was very small. It was several hours before any one of them could actually get down into the hull, and only then did they discover the little sliding door to the fo'csle. A wee bit apprehensively they slid the door open, only to find that the tiny compartment was completely empty, apart from one solitary, pathetic reminder.

From a nail in the bulkhead hung a fisherman's jacket of the usual navy blue serge, and in the oxter pooch there was a bonny set of mackerel flies, the hooks scarcely tarnished, and the multi-coloured feathers as bright and gay as ever.

'Look at this!' cries the younger boy. 'See fit I've gotten. I think this jacket micht fit me!' And he made as if he would don the jacket.

'Leave that aleen! Throw't awa!', says I, maybe a wee bittie sharp kind. So, with a peculiar glance at me the loon let the jacket drop to the sand. Within a few minutes it was completely buried, as the digging continued, but not before I had time to examine the bonny flies. The fingers that had made them had been masters of their trade, for the workmanship was exquisite. After a few moments of idle speculation, I dropped the neatly parcelled flies at my feet, where they too disappeared beneath the shovelled sand.

I left the scene early because, at that time, I was recovering from a major operation. In no way could I assist in the work, yet, in the morning, I was back on the beach to find a mystified Copper wondering who had put the jacket back on the nail. Of course, the mackerel flies were in the inside pocket. Did I ken onything aboot it?

When I simply shook my head, Copper called his elder son and bade him take the jacket up among the bents 'and bury the thing the richt gate!' This was duly done, and that day the last of the sand was removed from the boat's interior. The sea had been quietly doing some work all on its own, and now most of the boat was visible. An internal inspection revealed four broken frames and a few gaping seams. The engine, as expected, was one solid mass of rust and would have to be replaced; the rudder was missing, and the propeller had only one blade. But, in Copper's words, there wis naething that widna sort. Indeed,

the boatie was in remarkably good shape. A few strips of sheet lead and a few canvas patches would suffice to make her temporarily floatable.

At the end of the long day's darg, a satisfied Copper nailed a square of tarpaulin across the hatch, 'to keep ill-fashioned folk oot'.

'I'll see if I can get the len' o' a new-fangled digger the nicht, an' we can maybe get a start the morn to dig a trench to the sea.'

But, in the morning, the jacket with the bonny flies in the oxter pooch was back on the nail. There was no sign of the tarpaulin having been disturbed. Boys! Copper fairly swore that mornin'. With his new-fangled machine, he went well down the beach and dug a great hole in which to inter the jacket. He chose his spot well, for at high tide (he would never say 'High water'), it would be covered by several feet of water. Then he began to dig his trench from the boat towards the sea, so that the refloating operation might be expedited.

But, in the morning, the jacket, horn dry, was back on the nail. So Copper took it and soaked it with diesel before setting fire to it.

'That's the last o' that lot!' says he.

I had thought that he would give up, but I had misjudged my Copper. I'm sure he sensed and resented my stong disapproval, for when it came to arranging for a big boat to tow his prize off the beach, he bypassed me altogether and approached another of his former boyhood pals, Jericho Jake, skipper of the trawler *Dusky Rose*.

'Seein' that it's you, Copper, I'll dee't for a bottle o' fuskie!' says Jake, lachin'.

'I'll gie ye twa,' says Copper.

When the towing moment arrived, the boatie was sweir to move; sweir, sweir. But she couldn't resist the pull of five hundred horse-power on a tow-rope made of nylon, a substance we had never seen before. Much against her will, I thought, she was dragged bodily into the sea and towed into port.

'She'll hae t' lie there for a fylie!' says Copper. 'We're hine, hine ahin' wi' the Spring wark! Will ye keep an eye on her till I get time t' sort her?'

I said I would.

The *Dusky Rose* sailed that night for distant northern

fishing grounds and, you know, she never came back. Nobody knows how, nor why, nor where she was lost.

I'm sure this was the final straw which broke Copper's resolve, for when the Spring wark was finished, and the beasts were out in the parks, he came back to me just as I had expected.

'I'm nae seekin' the boat noo! Can we pit her back far we got her?'

I said that was well nigh impossible, even if he were allowed to try, but I did offer to help him in any way I could.

So Copper and his loons got their tractor and bogie again, and they loaded the boatie wi' rubble and great lumps o' granite, until she was just afloat and no more.

Then, with my ain boatie, we towed her north with the last of the ebb, and we sank her in twelve fathoms of water, hard against the south edge of the wicked reef which forms the Outers of Scotston Head.

On the way home, Copper was unusually silent, but suddenly he asked, 'Fit'll ye be needin' for this noo, freen'?'

'As far as you an' me's concerned,' says I, 'There's nivver nae chairge! Ye ken that, divn't ye?'

He nodded his head in acceptance, but didn't speak.

When we came abreast of the Queenie, I fired the question, 'Fit are ye thinkin' aboot noo, Copper?'

'Dam't!' says he, taken unawares, 'I'm jist winnerin' if yon jacket's back on the nail!'

Fit Like, Fairmer?

It was indeed a perfect day, warm and still. A few fleecy white clouds lay motionless over Mormond Hill, but otherwise the sky was a clear, deep blue. I had left Maud via the Honeyneuk Road and, having crossed the main road at the Shevado crossroads, I was on the ascent of the Reid Hull, that lofty eminence which affords a wonderful, panoramic view of the Buchan countryside. At the very top of the hill, at yet another crossroads, I drew my vehicle onto the patch of waste ground which was there for so many years, and switched off the engine. Not a sound now, but the sweet song of the lark, invisible in the blue.

Boys, what a view! Immediately in front, and to my left (on the port bow), lay the district of Corsegight, merging into other districts and parishes, right to the foothills of Bennachie. On my right, or starboard bow, lay the great spread of Balthangie. Simply by turning my head, I could look across the broad acres of Aalfat (Oldwhat) and the great, unbroken expanse of farmland reaching to the slopes of Mormond. Behind my left shoulder (on the port quarter), was the district of Stevensburn. Thus do crossroads divide the countryside into districts. Often, but not always.

No matter where I looked, I could see farmhouses, hundreds of them, spread out like a great fleet of ships at anchor, and I marvelled at the thought that every single one had its own water supply and its own waste disposal system. There's a lot more to farms than meets the eye. In the sweet green fields, great herds of cattle were grazing, and I wondered how the new 'Charlie' breed from France would please the fashious Buchan farmers. Oh aye! I kent a bittie aboot nowt! And I aye thocht the Herefords the bonniest.

But the cattle were not the only creatures in the parks. On every farm, as far as eye could reach, men were busy at the 'hyowe' (hoe), among the neeps, a weary, weary job awyte. This was a day when farmers would be in the neep parks in force, and few, if any would welcome the presence of any Traveller. Indeed, some of them didn't welcome Travellers at any time, and posted notices to that effect on their steadings. Still, I suppose, it tak's aa kinds. I once heard of a Traveller who called at a farm to ask for a contribution towards a wreath for a fellow Traveller who had passed away.

'Foo muckle wid ye be seekin'?', says the fairmer.

'Oh, mebbe half-a-croon,' was the reply.

'Weel!', says the fairmer, 'Here's ten shillin's. Ging an' bury ither three!'

Now, then, after some twenty minutes of viewing and musing, I took myself off, with the observation, 'This winna get a frockie t' the bairn!' But it was a rather fruitless errand I was embarking on. Past experience had taught me that, years ago. I was at a loss as to which district I should tackle, and, at the same time, I wished to justify my existence. So I finally decided to do a bit of poaching in a fellow Traveller's territory. It was possible that I might discover a prospective customer of whose existence my 'oppo' was blissfully unaware. It was a forlorn hope, but it was better than nothing. The poaching aspect didn't worry me in the least, for I knew that he did the same to me on a regular basis, under the fond illusion that 'Peter wid nivver ken!' That'll be the day! There's nae honour among thiefs!

Thus I found myself in foreign surroundings, on roads which I knew not, among places whose names were unfamiliar. It was an interesting trip, but a complete waste of time.

Then, suddenly, dead ahead, I spied a mannie who was making unmistakable signals that he desired to speak with me. 'Aha!', says I to mysel, 'This'll be a barrel o' ile, for sure!' So I drew to a halt beside him and remarked in my unbelievably pleasant baritone, 'Fit like, fairmer?'

He looks into my face, then he scans the name on my vehicle, an' says, 'Oh, it's you, is't. Esso!'

'Man, ye're richt!', says I. 'It's me, Esso! Every Saturday And Sunday Off. Div ye ken me?'

'No!', he says, 'But I ken aboot ye!'

'Fine!', says I. 'So we're half-roads there! Fit can I dee for ye?'

'Div ye ken onything aboot weemin?', says he. 'The wife's fair stucken, ye see!'

'Fit div ye mean, stucken? She canna weel be laired in a park in this dry wither, surely. Has she faan doon a hole or something?'

'Na, naething lik' 'at. She's jist fair stucken! Come in an' see if ye can help. I've phoned for the doctor, but it could be a fyle afore he gets here.'

Boys! I never saw a woman in yon state afore. She had been ficherin' among her floories wi' a fork, an' she was the same shape as a hair-preen. Her feet wis on the path, but her nose wis among the dusty millers, same as though she'd broken ower b' the pooches. Fair stucken, for she couldna win up!

'Good grief!', says I, 'Wid she nae been better t' boo her knees at that job?'

'Her knees is stucken anaa!', says he. 'I doot we're bate!'

'Nivver!', says I. 'We'll baith pit a hand on a hip, an' the ither hand alow her chin. Syne, if we baith heave thegither, that should tak' the kinks oot o' her!'

It didna! It fairly brocht a skirl, but that wis aa!

'Hiv ye nae an aul door aboot the place?', says I. 'We could cowp her ontill't an' cairry her into the hoose.'

'Nae sic a thing ava!', says he. 'There's a new door in the neep shed, but it wid be a shame t' blaad it!' An' he rins oot onto the road to look for the doctor. 'Nae sign o' the mannie, yet!'

'Weel!', says I. 'We'll cairry her in atween's, an' pit her inower the bed.' 'But we'll hae t' watch, cos if we pit her heid on the pilla, her feet'll hae t' be on the pilla anaa! If we turn her the ither road, wi' her dowp on the pilla, she'll be smored wi' the blunkits! Aye! We'll hae t' watch that!'

'She's fifteen steen!', says he, an' off he goes again to look for the doctor.

'We'll hae t' try something!', says I. 'We canna leave her like this!'

'Nae sign o' the doctor yet! Fit'll we dee noo? I dinna like the colour o' her face!', says he.

'It's the colour o' her drawers that I dinna like!', says I.

Boys! I must have said the necessary magic words, for yon wifie straightened up like a ramrod in two seconds flat, and came chargin' aifter me wi' the fork. I was lucky to make the safety of the van.

'Oot o' here, ye orra brute!', she says. 'I'll learn ye to speak aboot MY drawers!'

I got the engine started, but, before I took to the road, I screwed the window down and shouted, 'Ye're a peyed-thankless limmer! Fit wye could I see yer drawers fin ye're wearin' troosers?'

Mind over matter, boys, mind over matter! I've nivver been back along yon road again, but someday I'll ging in aboot an' cry, 'Fit like, fairmer?'

September

The summer's wearin' on, lass,
   The rodden's bonny reid
Comes lowein' thro' the greenery
   Abeen the quaet burn.
Yon reeshlin' barley's ripe, lass,
   It's fite, wi' hingin' heid.
Were I the fairmer here, lass,
   I'd tak' it in the morn.

It's surely nae a twalmont
   Since last we dauchled here?
It canna be a year, lass,
   Wis't nae jist late yestreen?
Ye seem t' think I'm wrang? Weel,
   I canna help but speir,
If that's the time that's flown awa,
   Then far's the sizzons geen?

It winna be that lang noo
   Afore the trees 'll stan'
In goons o' reid an' gold, lass,
   The wye they've deen afore,
Till rivin' win's come snarlin'
   Oot ower the shorn lan',
T' spread the bonny leaves like
   A bass at Winter's door.

A bittie like the barley,
   We're frail, wi' fitened heid;
A bittie like the trees, lass,
   Oor time for beauty's gone.
But lat's aye mind jist fit wis said
   Aboot the bruisèd reed,
An' nivver dread the Winter,
Tho' the summer's wearin' on.

September, 1985.

Hairy Tatties

Bring me a ling fae the Viking Bank,
A tusk fae the Patch or the Reef;
Or catch me a cod on the Buchan coast
An' I'll greet nae mair for beef.
Steep her in saut for a three-fower days
Then dry her slow in the sun
In the month o' Mey, fin the safter win's
Bring the green growth up thro' the grun'.

Bring me a bile o' the finest Pinks
Fae a craft on Mormon' Braes,
At the tail o' the hairst, fin the first fite frost
Tells a tale o' winter days.
Peel them an' bile in a fine big pot
Wi' my bonny fish in anither;
Bree them baith fin ye think they're richt,
Then ye'll chap them baith thegither.

A knottie o' butter an a glaiss o' milk –
Ye've a feast that's weel worth a Grace;
Then waste nae a meenit as ye fill yer speen
An' stap it into yer face.
Bring me a tusk fae the Patch or the Reef . . .
Fae the Viking Bank a ling;
Or catch me a cod on the Buchan coast,
Then I ken I'll dine like a king.

Lightning Strikes Twice

Sunday had been a richt bonny day, warm and still. In the soft, hazy sunshine the sea had shone like burnished steel with a straight, clear-cut edge. Was the horizon a wee bittie ower high? Well, maybe jist a thochtie, jist a thochtie. Could it be that this was a linen Sunday? If it was indeed a linen Sunday, we could expect a harn week for, according to tradition, the one would follow the other as night follows day.

All the world, with his wife and bairns, seemed to be 'oot for a traivel' on this fine day, the last day for several weeks that they would be together as families for, on the morrow, the greater part of the herring fleet would sail for East Anglia. A day or two later, special trains would carry great contingents of shore workers, guttin' quines and coopers, to the distant South and, by the end of the week, the Blue Toon would be seemingly deserted. Still, that had yet to come, and meantime, this was a day to be enjoyed. Lads and lasses were well to the fore among the throng, but the sweethearts went much further into the country than did the married folk, for all the cosy holes-and-bores among the still leafy hedge-rows were well outside the town. For most young couples, the morrow's parting would be only temporary; they would meet again in Yarmouth or Lowestoft.

I was one of the young fellas that day and, with my lass I took the long road round by Inverugie, returning via Mount Pleasant and the river bank. Oh, the roddens were bonny, and the corn stooks in the quaet parks reminded me of a Dutch scene on a tray which my father had once brought home from Ymuiden. It was a scene of pastoral tranquillity; it was a day to be enjoyed. And then I felt the 'slammach' on my face.

Slammach is the threads of fairy gossamer which may be seen clinging to the twigs of wayside bushes. It can also be seen glistening along the wire strands of a fence, or among the tansies, close to ground level. And even the fishermen in coastal waters can occasionally feel the slammach on their faces, slammach which is the herald of strong winds, usually accompanied by heavy rain. So this really was a linen Sunday, and a linen Sunday mak's a harn, or hessian, week. Seldom does the prediction fail.

I was one of the young lads of the day, but I was not going 'Sooth'. Not for me, the hustle and bustle of Yarmouth River and the fabled bright lights of the Prom and Britannia Pier. Not yet! Instead, I would be in a forty-foot seine-netter, fishing the inshore waters along the Buchan coast, mostly for plashies and soles, for we had yet to learn how to catch haddock and whiting. We did, however, cherish the hope that, from mid November until the New Year, the cod would seek their usual haunts between the Aal Castle (pronounce the 't') o' Slains and the Sands o' Forvie.

There were three of us in the boatie. First, there was Abadan ('cos he had sailed the Seven Seas). He was the cook, in that he biled the kettle, for we had no proper meals at sea. Every man cairried his ain piece and had a proper meal at home when the day's fishing was over. A practice ruinous on the gastric system. Abadan had the disconcerting habit of chewing the heads of matches, with a strong preference for Scottish Bluebell, almost unobtainable in the Blue Toon. In fact, he had asked one of his pals to bring him a hale packet o' blue matches fae Yarmouth where such things were in abundance.

Secondly, there was Jonnack, a lang, thin, quaet, hardy chiel; a grand worker with a vast repertoire of stories that wid gar yer hair curl. Jonnack's speech betrayed the fact that he was an incomer to Peterhead, for he called the monk-fish an 'oof', whereas I called it a 'caithick' and, when we got some coal in the net, as we often did, his word for the sickly-looking sea anemones thereon was 'pluffs'. I simply called them 'paaps'. I think Jonnack was originally a 'Duffer', but he wis neen the waar o' that.

Then there was myself, skipper/driver, quite a few years the junior of my shipmates. We had no demarcation lines as regards duties; all hands mucked in together.

Well, now, the high winds promised by the slammach didn't materialise until Monday was nearly spent but, when they did arrive, there were no half measures. We had had a reasonable day's fishing at the Castle Hard but, long before we reached home, we had 'plinty o' wither', even though we had a fair wind.

It was when we were rounding Buchan Ness that I missed Jonnack. Indeed, I thought he had gone overboard, so sudden was his disappearance but, praise be, he was still with us. He had been leaning, hands in pockets, against the wheelhouse, when his feet slid from beneath him and his left lug came yark doon the widwork. Lach? I nearly split my sides! And when, five minutes later, he did exactly the same to his ither lug, it was too good to be true. It must have been gey sair, but boys, it was comical.

All that night a strong southerly gale raged round the roof-tops, so fishing was out of the question on the Tuesday. We were scutterin' aboot the boatie when I fell oot on Jonnack.

'Hey!', says I. 'If ye dinna ging an' get a pair o' new boots, ye'll be needin' a pair o' new lugs. That black rubbish o' boots that ye're buyin', they're jist nae eese ava! Fitivver they be, they're certainly nae rubber, unless it's this new, artificial rubber we're hearin' aboot. The soles is worn smooth in nae time, then ye're forivver slidin' aa ower the place. Wid ye nae be better t' ging up t' Dunn's sale an' get a pair o' fite Dunlop boots? I ken they're dear. Aswarn they're a saiven-an'-twinty shillins, but they'll laist five times as lang as yon black trash.'

'Aye-aye', says Jonnack. 'Look fa's spikkin'! Saiven-an'-twinty shillins is maybe nae a lot t' you, but t' me, it's a gey lot o' siller! Ye'll need t' catch a hantle mair fish afore I can affoord gran' fite boots. We're nae aa like you, ye ken!'

Jonnack was richt, ye ken. He had a wife an' twa bairns; I was young, an' feel, an' single. We lived in two different worlds.

The hale day it blew, an' a great fleet o' Moray Firth boats socht shelter in Peterheid. On passage t' Yarmouth, the wither hadna bothered them muckle until they came roon Rattray Heid; then they got the win' in their face. The Blue Toon, they thocht, wis far aneuch for the nicht. The place wis jist stappit full o' strangers! Boys! I nivver thocht there wis so mony drifters in the Moray Firth, INS, BCK, an' BF. What a fleet!

Ye see, here was I, say twinty 'ear aal, an' I had nivver seen the Moray Firth ports. Oh, aye! I had been in Ireland an' the Isle o' Man. I had been in Stornoway, an' I had been in the Sooth Firth but, ye see, that had been wi' the boat. Twice had I been in Aiberdeen, but – I had nivver been in the Broch! To me, as to most of my generation, travel by land was a closed book.

Weel, noo, jist afore supper time, faa comes doon the pier but Jonnack, wi' a bonny pair o' fire-new, fite rubber boots. Prood as Punch wis he, as he stowed his new gear in the seat-locker in the foc'sle. Apparently him an' his Missus had heen a cooncil-o-war, a richt serious affair awyte, an' Jonnack had splashed oot!

'I got a twa-three bob aff,' says he. ''Cos I hiv sic aafa sma' feeties. I jist need a size six, an' they've been lyin' aboot the shop for a fyle!'

Noo, throwe the nicht, the wither eased awa so, fin we came doon in the mornin', t' ging t' the sea, the hale fleet o' strangers had sailed for Yarmouth.

And so had Jonnack's boots!

Boys! I'm tellin' ye, there wis nae lachin' that mornin'! Peer Jonnack could hardly speak ava! For him, it wis a proper disaster. As for me, I had never been so angry in my life! I must confess that, though I'm usually a quaet kind o' chiel, that wis ae time that I wis mair than willin' t' murder somebody, could I hae gotten my hands on them. Only the lowest o' the low wid steal a fella's boots!

'I'd jist as weel ging awa hame,' says Jonnack. 'I canna dee naething athoot boots.' Apparently he had dumpit the aal black pair.

Now, since there wis only the three o's aathegither, this meant that we wid be lowsed for the day. We couldna dee wi' less than three, an' even at that, we were sair made. An' forbye, the thocht wis in my mind noo, 'Far on earth's Jonnack gaan t' get anither pair o' boots?' The outlook wisna bonny!

Then, oot o' the blue, an idea came into my heid. The day wisna lost yet!

'Hold on, Jonnack!', says I. 'Nae ower fast! I've a pair o' boots at hame, that I got fae my father. They're leather boots, ye ken; knee boots, but I ken they're as ticht as a bottle. They're a wee bittie ower sma' for me, but they'll fit you fine. I'll be back in five meenits!'

So we finally got under way. Man, Jonnack likit the boots fine! They fitted jist perfect, but they were on the short side for his likin'. Ye see, Jonnack seldom wore an 'oilie', 'cos he thocht the oilskin frock wis ower close an' sweaty. So he jist wore the lang rubber boots b' themselves. Some lads likit an apron, but I aye thocht that to wear an apron near a winch was to invite disaster. Any man whose apron fouled the winch stood very little chance of escape.

Now, as it happened, we had a fair day's fishing, not by any means a fortune, but jist a 'day's mait' or, as the Duffers an' the Fitehills men micht say, 'A day's cost'. On the way home, we were in good spirits, although the matter of the stolen boots would rankle for mony a lang day.

'Fine booties ye've gien me!', says Jonnack. 'But I'll need t' get an apron, 'cos I'm weet fae the knees up. She'll read the Riot Act the nicht, fin she hears aboot the missin' boots!'

'Dinna tell 'er.' says I. 'She's nae needin' t' ken!'

'That's fit ee think,' says he. 'But she'll hae t' ken fit I'm needin' the fower-an'-six for. By jings, she wis sweir t' gimme the price o' the boots last nicht, but I'm thinkin' she'll ging throwe the reef the nicht! An', anither thing, I'm gaan t' dee fit ee dee; I'll tak the boots hame for safety!'

'Och!', says I, 'There's nae need for that, surely. Licht-

nin' nivver sticks twice in the same place!'

'Better safe than sorry!', says he.

So the boots gid hame, and as was to be expected, the storm broke ower Jonnack's heid. But, gradually the storm abated, and Jonnack got fower-an'six for a new apron (wi' the tows) fae Hutton the sailmaker in the Seagate. Sittin' at the fire that nicht, he spliced the towies into the shiny brass eyelets, aafa bonny. Then he fauled the apron fine an' ticht, an' stappit it into the leg o' the left boot. 'That's me aa riggit again!'

At the appointed time of half past three in the mornin', I met Jonnack at the boat, doon aside the aal Roon'hoose. Abadan was already there, and had the firie lichtit. Jonnack threw the teem boot doon onto the boatie's deck but, fin he threw doon the boot wi' the apron in't, sink me if it didna strick the first boot an' ging skitin' ower the side. Oh aye! It sank like a steen, an' oor efforts to retrieve it were in vain.

Comical, think ye? It wis naething short o' anither disaster, especially for a man wi' a wife an' twa bairns!

So lichtnin' nivver sticks twice in the same place?

Tell that to somebody else!

The Miraculous Catch

The propellers of the steam drifters were invariably made from cast iron, a metal eminently suited to the low revs of the steam engine and practically impervious to corrosion. But cast iron has one glaring fault – it will break rather than bend. In fact it will not bend at all. Thus it followed that a drifter's propeller could suffer irreparable damage if it fouled or struck any underwater obstruction.

Broken propellers were a common sight in the days of my youth. There used to be a puckle in the narrow triangle of ground where Charlotte Street and Maiden Street meet Kirk Street. That same triangle was at one time the town Dung Depot until the congregation of the nearby Muckle Kirk kickit up a stink aboot the stink. There was also a long row of damaged propellers leaning against the outside of the cemetery wall in the triangular scrap-yard which

adorned the west end of Landale Road. Fit did I say? A scrap-yard in Landale Road? That's richt, freen', jist opposite the present-day DHSS offices. The scrap-yard is now part of the Town Gardens. The propellers lay for years, simply because there was no known way of repairing them, and cast-iron has a very low scrap value.

When, in the thirties the motor boats began to make an impact on the fishing scene, stern-tubes, propellers and shafts were all made of bronze, an alloy of copper and tin. All the old fishermen called it brass, but brass is an alloy of copper and zinc, and that's not the same thing at all. Apparently the new metal was required for the high revs of the motor engines, and something called torque, whatever that may be. In any case, the new propellers were beautiful golden creations, but they didn't last very long.

Oh, they would bend and they were repairable, but they soon got 'aiten awa'. The highly polished blades became very badly pitted, so much so that holes would penetrate the blades, and parts of the tips would break off and disappear, leaving an edge as jagged as the lid of a tin that's been opened with a hammer and chisel.

Now, since it's the tips of the blades that do the work, these jagged propellers became highly inefficient. Boats lost their speed and their towing power until the inefficient prop was removed and built up, by means of brazing, to its original size. Then the whole corrosive process would start all over again.

Of course, the old fishermen said 'Fit ither could ye expect? The aul engineers used better metal. Jist rubbish ye get noo! The propellers on the aul Fifies an' Zulus laistit a lang, lang time'. Personally, I think that was because these old boats' propellers were as long out of the water as they were in it, coming, as they almost invariably did from harbours which were dry at low water.

Some bright sparks thought it must be an electrical problem since it coincided with the installation of dynamos and electric lighting. So they tried shifting the earth points here, there and everywhere; in fact they tried some weird and wonderful dodges, but all to no avail. The propellers still got aiten awa, worse on some boats than on others.

Now, with the post-war generation of motor boats growing steadily bigger, with triple the horse-power and consequently bigger propellers, the problem became really acute. You see, the three blades of a modern variable-pitch propeller (blades only, without the labour), will cost about £20,000, and you can't afford to let corrosion eat that. So the boffins got to work and, although it took them some time to identify the disease, they eventually came up with a cure.

It would appear that, if you put bronze into sea-water in close proximity to steel (rudders, keel-straps etc.), there is an immediate reaction called electrolysis which attacks the bronze. It doesn't do the steel any good either.

The cure is simple, as cures so often are. You simply get some blocks of zinc and bolt them to strategic points on the hull, not forgetting the rudder, and, Hey presto, the corrosion attacks the zinc and leaves the bronze alone. The zinc 'sacrifices' must not on any account be painted, since paint renders them useless. It's really amazing to see how soon the sacrifices become deeply pitted until finally they have to be renewed. But, all the time, the bronze remains intact.

I'm not qualified to give you technological explanations for this phenomenon, even if you wanted them, but next time you're near a slipway, have a look at the boats thereon and, when you see the zincs, you can point them out to your bairns and say, 'Zinc sacrifices, see?' Then you'll be a proper fountain of knowledge!

Now, there has to be a story, hasn't there? 'Aye! Surely!', says you. 'A true story? Ye wid nivver tell a lee,' says you.

Well, now, the story concerns the Boddam boatie *Fruition* PD173, a boatie that never got her proper name, for she was always called the *Frooshin*. Things like that disna bother the Boddamers, for they say 'tey' for 'tay', and they constantly use the word 'froonyil'. Still, they're nae the warst, an' ower the years I've been friendly wi' several o' their clan, one of whom was Jake, son of the *Fruition's* skipper, Reid Sonnie. In aa the years that I kent Jake, I nivver once saw him 'dressed' nor did I ivver see him athoot his Woodbine. A little bowleggit mannie wi' black teeth an' a Boddam twang as broad's the Broadgate, but a richt fine chiel for aa that. It was Jake that tellt me this story.

The *Fruition*, 37ft, with a 26/30 Kelvin paraffin engine, often went to the Firth of Clyde in the winter months to dredge for clams. The dredge is a fearsome contraption, somehow resembling the frame of an old-fashioned spring bed, only the frame is made of iron, and the 'spring' is a net of chain links. There are also sundry spikes for tearing the clams from the sea-bed. When the dredge is towed slowly along the bottom, the loosened clams rest on the chain meshes, but they cannot slide off because there's a top cover of heavy netting to keep them from escaping. That, very roughly, is a dredge.

Now, one very blustery morning, the *Fruition* was punching out of Ayr harbour and making a poor, poor job of it. She was plumping up and down, but making very little headway although the engine was at full throttle.

'Jake, my loon!', says aul Sonnie, 'Yer engine's nae gaan richt ava. Can ye nae get a bittie mair piff oot o' the thing? We'll nivver get oot o' here the day!'

'No, father,' says Jake. 'There's nae mair piff in 'er. It's the fan (propeller) that's vrang, cos it's aa aiten awa'. It's a new fan we're needin', for the boatie's awa' fae towin', an' if she canna tow her gear we canna possibly get clams.'

'A new fan?', says Sonnie. 'An' far div ye think that wid come fae?'

Jake had no reply, for times were hard indeed and a new propeller micht cost as muckle as £10. Good grief!

Eventually, aifter a sair, sair fecht, the *Fruition* reached the fishing grounds and commenced operations. The spirits of her crew were very low indeed, and when it was time to heave-up at the end of the first tow conversation was scarce. Aabody kent she had made a poor tow, so they could hardly expect t' get onything.

And how right they were. There were very few clams indeed, yet this was the best haul they had seen for many a long day, for there, all mixed up with the dredge was a bonny new propeller complete with some five feet of shaft. The propeller was precisely what was required to bring 'mair piff' to the *Fruition's* engine, so that afternoon she was beached in a certain port where, at low water, the old, corroded prop was removed and the new one fitted.

Jake made a few inquiries, casual kind, ye ken, and discovered that, some four months previously a twin screw motor launch had lost one of her propellers. When the propeller shaft breaks on board a single-screw vessel, it can slide out only a very short distance (say a foot or so) before the prop gets jammed on the rudder; but when the same break occurs on a twin-screw job, both shaft and propeller disappear, leaving the sea a great opportunity to pour in through the empty tube.

In this case the crew had managed to plug the tube and thus save the boat.

When Jake tellt me the story of his 'miraculous catch', I observed, 'Jake, that's the kind o' thing that nivver happens t' peer folk! To him that hath shall be given!'

Jake jist leuch, an' lichtit anither Woodbine.

*Zinc anodes (sacrifices) on a
fishing boat's hull.*

Entrance to South Harbour, Peterhead.

Russian factory ships (klondykers) in Peterhead Bay to purchase and process the herring caught by the modern Scottish fleet. 1988.

Calcium Carbide

When I was a boy, there was a wide-spread belief that, if you took a bittie o' carbine and shoved it doon a herrin's throat into its belly, any skurry silly enough to eat such a doctored fish would disintegrate in a few seconds before your very eyes. The 'skurry' is, of course, the common gull. Now, in those distant days, getting a supply of herring to throw away was no problem; you could get herring lying around all over the place. But to get a bittie o' carbine as an explosive charge was a little more difficult, for carbine was a most important substance, certainly not for little boys to throw away. I must confess that, in my time, I have primed a few herrings with carbine and thrown them to the gulls, but never have I seen any burst of guts and feathers. This has taught me two things; firstly, that the skurry will eat practically anything, and secondly, that some folk like to spread false doctrine.

The 'carbine' in question was actually calcium carbide, a compound of carbon with something else whose identity I have never known. This useful substance was universally called 'carbine', and it came in sealed, hundred-weight drums, half as high again as a five-gallon oil drum. Carbine was a very hard substance which rattled in the drum when the drum was rolled along the deck. Something like coal in appearance, only not quite so black, carbine was magic stuff which, on contact with water, produced acetylene gas which burned with a brilliant white flame. This gas was the main source of lighting on fishing boats for many, many years, just as it was the best lighting for millions of bicycle lamps before the arrival of the torch battery. Not until the Hitler war was over did electric light appear on the steam drifters, and by that time the drifters themselves were in the latter stages of their lives.

On the *Meadowsweet,* as on all drifters, the gas plant was at the foot of the engine-room ladder, beneath the starboard side-deck. Hand-made by skilled tinsmiths, these gas plants were highly efficient and very simple.

In an open-topped drum (say, the size of a 40 gallon oil barrel), another open-ended drum, slightly smaller than the first, was inverted in some eighteen inches of water. Bolted to the outside of the outer drum, two metal boxes with air-tight covers served as containers for the carbine, and were drip-fed with water from a little brass tank. When the charge in one box was exhausted, the water supply could be diverted to the reserve box while the spent charge was removed and replaced with fresh carbine. The gas generated in the charge-boxes was piped up through the water into the inner drum which then floated on a cushion of gas, gas which could not escape except by means of the feed-pipe to the various lighting points throughout the ship. There were no mantles, simply the naked flame from special 'fish-tail' burners.

The engine-room, cabin, galley and binnacle had one light apiece, and there were two hauling-lights on the front of the wheelhouse. With very rare exceptions, all other lights were paraffin lamps. By today's standards, such a lighting system would be hopelessly inadequate but, in its day, it was the best available.

Empty carbine tins made excellent buckets for the dumping of ashes and clinker from the boiler furnaces. On each side of the 'casing', slightly aft of the funnel, the drifters had a tall, cowl-shaped ventilator for bringing fresh air to the stoke-hole and draught to the furnaces. In the shaft of each ventilator, just above casing height, there was a little door which opened outwards and, in the shaft, immediately above the door, there was a pulley and a rope with two hooks. Thus the fireman, standing on deck could hoist the buckets of ashes via the ventilators and empty the refuse into the sea. The chief, of course, filled the buckets in the warmth of the stokehole.

Carbine tins were also in great demand on shore, for they made excellent aise-buckets in the days when polythene bags were unknown. Even in the 'select' streets, ranks of carbine tins stood along the edge of the pavement awaiting the scaffies. From the scaffies' point of view the tins were a disaster, for they held too much, and thus were rather heavy.

Then there is the true story of how a certain Aberdeen trawler called at the Blue Toon in search of an extra crewman, having left her home port, one short of the required number. Well, the fella who readily accepted the berth (a pier-heid jump), had no sea-boots, but he somehow managed to carry out his duties by standing in two carbine tins. There you see the resourceful Bluemogganer at his glorious best.

Well, now, our dissertation on carbine and its uses brings us to the fireman, or stoker on the *Meadowsweet*. Although he actually merited the title of second engineer, he was universally known as 'the fireman', whose duties were varied and very many. He was responsible for all the lights on the vessel, both gas and paraffin; he cleaned the furnaces and hoisted out the ashes; he took watch and watch with the chief and, while the deck squad were hauling the nets, he coiled the heavy messenger rope in the bush-rope locker. A very busy man indeed.

Most firemen eventually rose to be chiefs in their own right, but Lugs, the Turk's fireman seemed to have no desire for promotion. He had been given his nickname for obvious reasons, but he was a richt fine chiel, a grand worker and a first-class shipmate. An incomer to the Blue Toon, he took great pride in proclaiming that his birthplace was Finechty (Findochty), the Holy City, far we hiv 'Oor ain stroop wallie an' oor ain kirk hallie'.

Some folk would have said that peer Lugs had been jist thrown awa', for he had mairried a Peterheid quine that wisna jist the berry. She likit t' lie in her bed wi' a quarter o' chocolate bon-bons an' a copy o' the Red Letter. Jist reid rotten, she wis. Her name wis Fandolina Butterworth, but to Lugs she wis jist 'Dolly'. There wis ae Saiterday that Lugs got hame early-kind (say aboot eleven o'clock in the foreneen), an' boys, he didna half get a shock, for Dolly wis up, an' fit's mair, she hid the fire lichtit. In fact, it wis a great muckle bleeze o' a fire, an' Dolly wis sittin' in front o't, brakkin' her hairt.

'Oh, Dolly darlin',' cries Lugs. 'Fit's adee wi' ye the day?'

'Ooh me, ooh me!', cries she, 'I'm burnin'.' Reid rotten, sure as daith! But Lugs jist adored his Dolly, an' it's maybe jist as weel!

Lugs wis come o' a famous fisher faimly. In fact his Granda scored a great victory ower the Aul Enemy at Yarmouth. Granda wis skipper o' a Zulu boat that had jist left Yarmouth River fin the win' fell flat calm, an' the rain came doon in buckets – jist hale watter! The hale crew disappeared below, leavin' Granda sittin' like a prize doo at the helm. Sail boats had nae wheelhooses, so Granda jist had t' tak' 'is shak' wi' the wither.

Up comes a fire-new English drifter, een o' the very first o' the kind, wi' a Woodbine funnel. The shippie wis heavy wi' herrin', an' wis homeward bound at seven knots. Her skipper, prood o' his big shot, prood o' his new ship, an' mair than prood o' his fancy wheelhouse, steered close past the becalmed sail-boat an' shouted in derision at the forlorn, dreepin weet mannie in the starn.

'Where's yer umbrella this mawnin', Scottie?'

'Oh, dam't', cries Granda. 'I clean forgot! I left it wi' your missis last nicht!' One - nothing for Finechty!

Now let's get back to Lugs. When the news broke, that Dolly was expecting, there were sidelong glances and sly winks among Lugs' shipmates. There were also a few unkind, speculative remarks in Lugs' absence, but the Turk silenced them all with the shrewd observation, 'Ye're aye sure o' the mither'.

Came the long awaited morning when, in their single room in Threadneedle Street, Dolly gied Lugs a great dunt in the ribs an' tellt him t' get the Doctor. Lugs ootower the bed like a shot an' hauled his breeks on, then he shivved his feet intill his carpets an' set oot! He didna tak' time even t' fasten his galluses; he jist held his breeks at the front wi' ae hand while the ither hand flailed like a piston, an' his galluses streamed in the breeze.

Boys, he wis gaan like the verra haimmers but, seein' that he had his carpets on, he couldna hear his feet, so he thocht he wisna movin'. That gart him run even faster, so it wis in a state o' collapse that he reached the Doctor's hoose in Queen Street. There he gied the bell a good, hard dirl; then, thinkin' that the bell wisna workin', he startit haimmerin' at the door wi' his niv. There wis nae instantaneous response, so he thocht he wid try baith nivs, but syne his breeks fell doon roon his cweets, an' he wis jist bendin' doon t' haul them up fin the door opened.

Apparently unruffled by the question-mark posture of the caller, but obviously amazed at the shocking pink colour of the drawers on display, the Doctor says, 'Judging by appearances, and by the fearful racket, this must be an urgent call'.

A wee bittie short o' breath, Lugs jist nodded.

'Is it a confinement, then?'

'Oh, no, Doctor!' cries Lugs. 'It's nae naething lik' 'at! It's a bairn!

Since this story was written, I have learned from 'Pilot', an old friend in Lossie that the Lossie loons were at the same caper, feeding 'loaded' herrings to the gulls. The only real difference was that the Lossie loons kept a close watch on the poor birds, which invariably settled on a pier which was seldom used, and there, after a short interval, the chest and belly would disintegrate.

I'm glad I loaded only a few herring.

The Heid Case

All day long the ship-to-ship radio waves had been a proper Babel of sound as scores of skippers sought to converse with their pals. These were the days before the advent of VHF with its multiplicity of channels – the days when inter-ship communications were restricted to two, or maybe three wavebands. It defies description, the rabble on the air from at least a hundred boats in an area some twenty miles by twelve, especially when matters were made even worse by the close proximity of an Armada of foreigners, all at the same game – nattering on the radio. Scotsmen and Englishmen, Frenchmen, Dutchmen and Belgians all mixter-maxter off the coasts of Northumberland and Durham. Fyles it was gey sair on the lugs, but you simply had to know what your fellow man was doing; was he shooting or hauling, was he fast in a wreck, or was he just lying there licking his wounds?

You see, it was late summer, and the herring were in abundance in that area. A considerable fleet of Scotch and English drifters were after the herring by night; the foreign trawlers were after the herring night and day, and a host of seiners from all over the place were after the cod which were after the herring. Poor herring! The seiners fished in daylight only. Some of the foreigners didn't want the cod which they sometimes caught in their trawls, and it was not unknown for them (usually a Dutchman) to call a Scotch boat to come alongside and get a few score of prime beauties. Dunkirk and Normandy and all that, you see.

Now it was evening, and the seiners were in harbour for a few hours' sleep, prior to landing their fish. The sea was left to the drifters and the foreigners, but long before the drift nets were hauled, the seiners would be on the go again. But the rabble of voices didn't cease – it was simply transferred to the Mission canteen where fishers, from Nairn to Sunderland met for a wash and a news over a cup of tea or a bottle of Quosh and a baggie o' crisps. The place was like a beehive, and in the buzz of voices it was difficult to hear yourself speak. Every conceivable East coast dialect was in full swing.

'Hey, Peter!', says a Fitehills skipper, 'I've an aafa job kennin' fit iss mannies is sayin'. Ye ken, the mannies fae Seahooses an' Newbiggin' an' Amble. Maist o' them seems t' hae a hurl in their throats, an' I'm gey sair made t' mak' them oot. Div 'ee ken fit they're sayin'?'

'Fine that!', says I. 'I've kent the men for 'ears, but I'm sure you newcomers disna ken a word apairt fae the sweers. The hurls an' the habbers disna bother me ava!'

Fishermen, even English fishermen, are not exactly at home in Standard English. Oh, they can use it, all right, but they prefer to use their own dialect. Now, that's fine until you want to speak to someone whose dialect is unfamiliar to you, just as yours is to him. Then you must resort to your 'proper' English, which is probably 'a bittie roosty for the want o' eese', and then you'll begin to feel a bittie self-conscious cos the hale North Sea's listenin' an' sayin', 'Jist hearken t' yon pansy "talking".' And then you'll tell yersel that this fella that ye're spikkin' till maun be some kine o' twit. Jist fit he's thinkin' aboot you.

Somebody spread the word that in their midst there was a man who had no language problems, and I was immediately co-opted as Honorary Interpreter! Any skipper, Scotch or othewise, would enlist my services when a translation was required. I thought it was a great joke, and went to the counter for a bottle of fizz from the steward, a peculiar man who went about his duties with a marmalade cat draped across his shoulders.

Suddenly the hubbub in the canteen ceased and, as I turned to see the reason for the silence, I heard the steward mutter 'Cor! Stone the crows! I'd better get the Boss!'

My govies! It was 'Stone the crows', sure enough, for every eye in the place was on the strangest figure I have ever seen. He had just come through the swing doors and was making his way slowly between the tables, obviously looking for the Mission man. His jersey proclaimed that he was English, for it reached almost to his knees, while the sleeves stopped short at the elbows. Moreover, the neck was three sizes too wide. No Scot would be seen dead in such a garment. A few scales on his boots told us that he was a herring man, but nobody was looking at his boots, but at his head.

The top of the poor man's head was as flat as if a girder had fallen on it, and that part which should have been above the level of his ears was now sticking out at the back in a grotesque lump, swathed in a polka-dot hanky. Mind you, it's a gey lump if ye can rowe a cloot roon't.

'Good Lord', says the Mission mannie, hastily summoned. 'Whatever happened to you?'

'Fell head first down the hold, didn't I?' says the casualty.

The Mission man immediately phoned for a doctor, mentioning the words 'Ambulance' and 'severe injury'. Then he questioned the poor fellow, 'Are you all alone? Where's your skipper?'

'Gone to sea and left me to fend for myself. Just put me ashore and cleared off! Skipper's a hard, cruel man. No time for anyone who's hurt or sick. Slave driver.'

At this there was a buzz of indignation among the fishermen. Never had any of us heard of such callousness. Any man who could leave a shipmate in such an appalling state should be hung, drawn and quartered. Several quiet men who had never been known to swear expressed their feelings clearly and vividly.

On the arrival of the doctor, the patient was taken into a side room, then, after a very cursory examination he was sent off to hospital for specialist treatment. Thereafter we all went to our boats for a sleep.

Next morning, at sea, I was amazed to find that the Interpreter's job was mine in reality. The Moray Firthers

hadn't been joking after all! Problem after problem was thrown at me from all quarters. 'Peter, tell me fit iss mannie's sayin'.' 'Peter, will you tell your Highland tribesmen to stop using Gaelic!' Boys they were referring to Duffers and Cullen men! At first it was amusing, but the novelty soon wore off, especially since I had enough problems of my own. And besides, I had a strong suspicion that some skippers, on both sides, were having me on. Then I realised that I had tremendous powers at my disposal. What if the interpreter is not the soul of honour? What if the poor soul thirsting for a clear translation gets a really crazy answer? I decided to find out.

On the third morning I was busy trying to get a big Frenchman to alter course, otherwise he would tow through our gear. I was vaguely aware that, somewhere in the background, Jackie from Newbiggin was telling a Duffer in no uncertain terms where he should go. Apparently there were problems, but the biggest problem was that Jackie, besides having a distinct hurl, had also a fearsome habber, so the peer Duffer was clean raivelt. In an unbelievably plaintive tone, and in a pure Macduff tongue the expected question arrived, 'Are ye wiggin', Peter? Fit's iss that Jackie's bleeterin' aboot the day?' On the spur of the moment I replied, 'Och, Bill, he's jist speirin' if yer Grunny still gings t' the duncin'.' There were no more requests for translations, for I was instantly demoted.

That afternoon, dense fog brought seining to a halt. With such a throng of boats in such a restricted area it was considered too dangerous to carry on, for at that time none of us had radar and collisions would have been inevitable. Most skippers, therefore decided to grope their way to harbour and safety. Just after tea-time, when the hubbub in the Mission was approaching its usual pitch, a burly stranger entered. Nobody paid the slightest attention as he made his way to the counter. He was just another stranger, and strangers were ten a penny. But the sound of the Mission man's voice raised in anger brought a sudden hush to the place.

'So you're looking for your cook, skipper? How noble! How noble indeed, to come looking for the poor lost sheep after four days! It's mercy and forgiveness you should be seeking, after what you did to that poor soul!'

'So you HAVE seen him, then?'

'Indeed, I've seen him! We have all seen him, and we are all amazed that such cruelty should exist in this enlightened age. You should hang your head in shame!'

'Where is he now? In hospital?' says the skipper.

'Where else would he be with head injuries such as he had? Certainly he's in hospital, and eminent consultants from Edinburgh have been to see him. They're studying his case very closely, since it is more or less unique!'

'Who put him in hospital, friend?'

'I did!' says the Missioner proudly. 'He's in the right place, getting proper attention and loving care.'

'How soon do you think you could get him back, friend?'

Boys! I thocht the Mission mannie wid burst. I'm sure dogs widna hae lickit yon skipper's bleed, aifter fit the mannie caaed him!

'Look here!' says the skipper, patiently. 'You put my cook in hospital! Now, will you please get him back as soon as possible? For the past few days we've landed our herring in another port, but now we're going home. Tell him that, if he comes now, I'll take him home in the ship; otherwise he'll have to pay his own fare! He didn't have no accident! He didn't fall down no hole! He was born with his head out of shape, man. This is the third time he's played this trick on me. When he gets fed up, he goes ashore in a strange port where there's a Mission and spins a tale of falling down a hole, of callous shipmates and cruel skipper, till somebody bungs him in hospital. Oh boy, he loves to be coddled by the nurses and fed like a fighting cock! I knew where he was when I missed my spotted hanky. Now, Missioner, do I or do I not get my cook?'

Within the hour the shippie sailed with a full complement. I spoke to the skipper just before he left the Mission.

'He must be an exceptionally good cook, when you put up with these didoes.'

'He's not even a decent cook,' says he, 'but he IS my wife's brother'.

Poor skipper!

Hielan' Briggie

It's a briggie ower a ditch, an' that's jist aa.
A shortcut fae the pier to the hotel.
There's a railin' on baith sides, for fear ye faa,
But I'm thinkin' some kind wizard's cast a spell,
For it's nae a timmer briggie, it's a Coach for Fairyland;
A larry, load wi' Jaffa Cakes, a Ship to Samarkand.
It's a Shoppie; it's a Hoosie that has aathing but a fridge;
A special Run to Scourie, or the Bus to Bonar Bridge.
It's a Van like Postman Pat's, wi' sweet Fancy for its load.
Man!, I leave things to the driver, for she fairly kens the
    road.

'Ye wis born ower seen!' they tell me. 'Mair than fifty 'ear
    ower seen.
Had ye come a lifetime later . . . Man, faa kens fit micht
    ha' been?'
But it's deil the word I'm hearin', . . . I'm at Cinderella's
    Ball,
On a shakkin' Hielan' briggie . . . wi' my fower-'ear-aal.

Parson Grey

To see a side-deck brimming with herring in the light of a summer dawn is to see the unforgettable. Solid silver, burnished silver, living silver, with flashes of brilliant blue and emerald and with subtle hints of pink; herring as shore-folk can never hope to see them; King Herring. The haddock also is a vision of delight whose silver is only slightly less brilliant, merging into grey and pink, the whole enhanced by the distinctive side-striping and the mark of Peter's thumb, as bold and clear as a birth-mark.

The humble podlie has no such elegance. Born a buddick, it passes through the podlie stage to become a saithe and finally a black-jack, alias coaley, green cod or rock-salmon. I may have my evolutionary theory all mixed up there, but it matters little, I'm sure. The podlie is the fish which little boys catch and throw away; the podlie is despised by the fisher-folk, as a rule. And why? Purely and simply because of prejudice! 'Oh, gyaad', for no clear reason.

Well do I remember how Johnny Taylor gave me a 'bile o' hard fish', caught at the Scaurs o' Cruden and dried on the sunny braes at Finnyfaul. They were perfectly delicious but – Johnny shouldna tell't me they were podlies. See what I mean?

Still, for some fisher-folk the podlie was a vital factor in the household economy. No!, my friend, not in the days of Dickens or Mark Twain, but in the twenties and thirties of this century. Let me tell you about Simon, a friend whose conversation I really enjoy, simply because it recalls an era which has never been properly recorded and is thus in danger of being utterly forgotten.

Now, if it's the guessing game you're after, just forget it. I have a host of friends, all along the coast, a something I'm rather proud of. So, when I tell you that Simon speaks of 'podlas' instead of 'podlies', you can stop looking for him in the Blue Toon.

Simon's 'ages wi' me', or possibly a wee bittie younger. I ken we've baith the same colour o' hair. Simon wis brocht up in a hard, hard school; so much so that, at the age of seven he could dee ony mortal thing wi' a smaa-line. Only his mither could beat him at the baitin', but

then she wis a real flier! In the butt-an'-ben the unbreakable rule was 'Work or want'. Work there was in plenty, and Want was never far fae the door.

The eldest in a long line of sons, Simon soon became his mother's confidant and his father's right-hand-man. As his brothers grew up, Simon trained them as he himself had been trained, – hard! While still at a tender age the senior loons wid hire a sheltie an' a trap for the day (one-and-sixpence) an' ging roon the country sellin' the podlas they'd catched themsel's. Oh aye, they had to feed the horsie, but there wis aye plinty o' girss at the roadside, an' forbye, some o' the country-folk wid gie the craiter a tasty bite o' corn or hey. The country-folk's nae greedy, ye ken.

But the maist important thing aboot the country-folk wis that they likit podlas. Bein' country-folk, they kent aafa little aboot fish, so they relished the fishies that the ignorant fishers despised. The verra best o' fish, fresh fae the sea! But, as a rule, nae on a Saiterday; ony ither day but Saiterday. Thus did the loons come t' ken a richt lot o' country-folk. An' the siller they earned? Mither got the lot; ivvery maik!

In the summer months, when herring were plentiful, the loons would go into the Toon to scran a puckle herring from the drifters. Cut into small pieces, these herrings made grand bait for the smaa-line. Any surplus bait was put to good use; nothing was wasted. While Simon's father stood out of sight just inside the doorway, the tempting morsels of herring were suddenly scattered on the open ground in front of the house. This brought to earth an immediate frantic squabble of screeching gulls, fighting each other for a share; then even as they fought they were laid low by a sudden shot-gun blast from the doorway. 'Roon the doors noo, loons, an' seek thrippence apiece for the myaaves.' Anyone fancy a gull? 'Oh, gyaad,' did ye say? Ye've surely nivver been hungry!

Came the sudden midnight knock on the door one wintry night, when a country couple more than half-way home had been driven back by a snow-storm.

'We've tried a gweed puckle doors, but aabody's tell't

us t' come here! It's nae this nicht we'll win hame; could ye possibly tak's in till mornin'?'

'Oh aye! Surely! Come in an' get a heat at the fire, syne ye'll get a bide (bed) for the nicht!'

Now, Simon's bed was the lowest of a tier of three bunk-beds in what purported to be a 'middle closetie' atween the butt and the ben. He could actually reach out and open the door without getting up. So Simon lay and racked his brains as to where this promised bide would come from. Finally he tackled his father on the quiet – 'Da, ye ken there's bides aawye in this hoose, an' ilkie bide's full! Ye jist dinna hae a spare bide t' gie this folk!'

'Oh aye, my loon, there's a spare bide – There's your een! Ee can sleep up in the laftie amon' yon twa-three bits o' net. Ye surely widna like me t' turn the folk awa, wid ye?' And that was how it was.

Simon has told me more than once how, on a Saturday evening, his mother would bait the line for Monday morning. No such work would be done on Sunday, for that was the Day of Rest. The line baited, she would rise from her stool, her stockings soaking with mussel bree. Then, while Simon stowed the line in a safe place, his mother would dig deep into the side-pocket of her ample skirt for her purse, from whose tattered interior she would lay coins in 'little heapies' along the edge of the dresser.

'That's for the butcher, the baker, the grocer and the milk.' Always in that order, and more often than not, the purse was left almost empty.

As eldest son, Simon had been delegated to keep an eye on the level of the oatmeal in the 'girnal', the copious meal-barrel which every family had. If ever the level seemed dangerously low, he was to warn his mother, who would 'gie him siller t' get meal fae the mull'. For a long time Simon had neglected this duty; it had never been really necessary. But one memorable week, when a combination of scarce fish and bad weather decreed that there should be no income for the household, Simon peeped into the girnal only to find it empty.

'Mither!' he cried, anxiously, 'Div ye ken the girnal's teem?'

'I ken, my loon, I ken. Ye hinna been watchin', hiv ye?'

'Will I rin t' the mull, Mither?' But the look on Mither's face froze the words in his throat, an' he grat.

'Dinna greet, my loon, dinna greet. I got aneuch meal oot o' the girnal the day t' dee the morn's brakfist, but I ken it's teem noo. I've jist heen a wordie wi' the Lord aboot it.'

She was that sort of woman, was Mither – the disconcerting type who speak about the Lord as if He were a member of the family, not in any bold, impudent familiarity, but simply because they consider that He actually IS a family member.

The first time you meet such folk you may be tempted to giggle, but very soon you'll realise that you're the one who's at a loss for words, you're the one who's ill-at ease, and you're the one who's face-to-face with a something you cannot handle. All my life, all along the coast, I have known such-like, and I think they're the very salt of the earth. Let me tell ye something else about them; they're not restricted entirely to the coast, but they're scarce-kind among the better-off class. Aawye!

'Mither', sobbed Simon, 'I doot ye've left it ower late this time!' In his mind's eye, the loon could see the edge o' the dresser bare on Saturday night, and he couldna thole the thocht.

'Ye ken this is Friday nicht, Mither, divn't ye?'

'Jist wyte an' see, my loon, wyte an' see!' It was a very dejected Simon that fell asleep in the middle closet, that nicht!

But at two o'clock in the morning the loon was roughly shaken awake by his father, who seemed somehow to have lost his reason.

'C'mon, loon, get yer claes on. We're gaun doon amon' the rocks t' catch podlas! Hing in, noo!'

Simon quickly realised that only the youngest boys were to be exempt from duty. The four who could handle a line efficiently were the conscripts on a fool's errand. Fisher-folk widna look at podlas; country-folk widna tak' them on a Saiterday. Surely the 'aul-man' ocht t' ken better! But since he had never seen his 'aul-man' like this afore, the loon held his peace.

For almost four hours, with rotten bait, Father and four sons catched podlas (the podlie is not a fastidious eater). Steadily the tally mounted till Father called a halt.

'C'mon, loons, lat's get this lot hame!'

Thus was broken the long resentful silence. At the rear of the house, the fish were split and cleaned, and there they lay in basins and in basketies, each one fresh and wholesome in its parson-grey shroud.

Breakfast was a silent fiasco. Three of the youngsters sat fast asleep, spoon in hand, their foreheads on the table, their porridge untouched. Simon could barely stay awake; Father said nothing.

Suddenly, on the door there was a hard, sharp knocking, strongly reminiscent of the knocking in the snowstorm, and there stood McClure, the big important Fish Merchant fae the Toon.

'Boys!' says he. 'A chiel fae the country's come in on me this mornin', an' he's needin' podlas, a hantle o' podlas. Apparently some folks come hame fae New Zealand, an' ithers fae Canada, an' somebody's come up wi' the idea that they should hae some kind o' gran' Re-union Dinner. Noo, t' mak' things like aul times, they wid like podlas, and' there's nae sic a thing t' be gotten. Div ye think you lads could catch a puckle, an' I'll come back for them?'

'Come an' see this,' says Father. 'Is this fit ye're lookin' for?'

'Far the Hell?' says McClure, but he didna sweer twice. Nae wi' Mither listenin', 'That's exactly fit's nott! I'm thinkin' the half o' the country's gaun t' this Do. Jist the verra dunt, boys, the verra dunt.'

'Weel,' says Father, 'Tak' them awa! But unnerstan' this! Neist wik winna dee wi' the siller! We're needin' the siller NOW!'

McClure understood, specially fin he saw the sleepin' bairns. (They were only bairns, fin aa wis said an' deen.) An', to be fair to the man, he gied them a rale gweed price.

So the edge o' the dresser wisna bare that nicht, aifter aa. An', fit's mair, the girnal wis full. Fin Simon wis fillin' the barrel, his Mither chided him gently.

'So I left it ower late, Simon? Maybe some day ye'll learn that the Lord disna work wi' the clock!'

It was years later that Father confided to his right-hand-man.

''T wisna me that gart ye rise an' catch yon podlas. Twis Mither that jist widna rest. Od, loon, ye wid ha' thocht she kent something!'

The Witch-Doctor

It was Saturday forenoon and it was raining very heavily. The crew of the *Meadowsweet,* having landed their twenty-cran shottie and washed out the hold, were gathered in the wheelhouse awaiting the skipper's return from the office. The cabin was temporarily out-of-bounds, for Jeemsie was busy scrubbing it out. The Turk had gone to the office for the crew's 'stoker' (perks), cash from the sale of mackerel, of which there had been quite a few, that week. Mackerel always belonged entirely to the crew, who would wait very patiently indeed for the few bob that would come their way.

Meanwhile, their topic was Hector, one of their number who had been sent home by the skipper as soon as the vessel had reached port. 'Nae lookin' neen weel ava'; 'the colour o' daith'; 'time he saw the doctor', were some of the comments. Then, when Jeemsie had given the 'All

clear', the lads made their way aft to the cabin, where each man removed his sea-boots, thoroughly hosed clean, and donned his go-ashore footwear. Most of them removed their pillow slips which would serve as containers for the few personal effects (towels etc), they would take home. Clean gear would be substituted on Monday.

'So Hector's nae-weel?' says Jeemsie. 'Nae muckle winner! His tongue's like a harled wa', an' his breath has a smell like a teem gut-barrel. It's a miracle we're nae aa nae-weel ower the heids o' him. An' forbye he's a foosty aul fizzer. Aswarn he's abeen fifty, an' ony man o' that age shouldna be here ava. If he'd only sense, he should ken that he'll seen be awa t' the happy land sellin' tripe. He should be lookin' for a quaet corner t' dee in, instead o' fartin' aboot amon' bowse an' tows an' scalders!'

Not until it was too late did Jeemsie realise that the

Turk, light-footed as a cat despite his bulk, was standing close behind him listening very, very attentively to the youngster's dissertation.

'Oh, I didna mean you, skipper; an' I didna mean you either, Sonnie!' cries the loon. 'Oh jingers!' And he fled up the trap to the galley.

'Ye needna think muckle o' yersel's', says the Turk to his crew, among the hearty laughter which followed. 'Accordin' to yon spleeter o' win', it's hardly worth hiz lads gaun hame! Hi, Jeemsie, come awa doon an' get yer siller.

Jeemsie kent that there wid be nae 'stoker' for him unless he came to collect it, so he had to yield. Down the trap he came, wi' a self-conscious grin on his face.

'Noo, my loon,' says the Turk, as he laid Jeemsie's share on the table. 'Hiz foosty aul fizzers is aafa teen on wi' yer gran' speech; in some wyes it wis true, an' in ither wyes it wis clivver, but it wis far ower sair on Hector. The peer sowl's maybe lyin' at daith's door noo, for aa that we ken. Could a great intellect like yours nae come up wi' a spot-on diagnosis o' Hector's trouble, seein' that ye ken so muckle aboot aul deen men?'

'Nae bother ava,' says the loon. 'Fine div I ken fit's wrang wi' Hector. He's fair corkit, that's aa.'

'An' hoo dis Sherlock Holmes arrive at that conclusion? Please elu, elu, explain to hiz lesser mortals, kind sir!'

'Weel, it's iss wye,' says Jeemsie. 'Ivvery Monday mornin', fin Hector comes doon, he gies me a Saiterday's Gazette (Evening Express) t' pit in alow his pilla, for his ain private an' personal use. Syne, on Friday or Saiterday he comes t' me speirin' if I've a bit o' an aul Rover or Wizard t' gie 'im. He hisna come t' me this week, an' if ye look aneth his pilla, ye'll see the Gazette hisna been touched. I'm tellin' ye, Hector's fair corkit!'

'Govey Dicks! It's as weel I tell't 'im t' see the doctor,' says the Turk.

'He tellt me he wis gaun t' see the Witch-Doctor, yon droggist mannie,' says Duncan. 'He says the doctor 'll jist gie 'im a paperie t' tak' t' the droggist, an' that means peyin' twice, so he's cuttin' oot the middle man.'

'It's oot t' the Boddam quarry he should ging, – for dynamite,' says Jeemsie. 'I'm awa hame.'

'I'll see Hector mysel',' says the Turk. 'He'll be lookin' for 'is stoker. Hector's jist like the rest o's, inclined t' lat things rin on ower lang, so I'd better hae a word wi' Margit.'

But alas, the Turk fell asleep (as usual) aifter he got his denner, so it was evenin' afore he got the linth o' Hector's. The patient wis lyin' in the box-bed in his worsit draars an' flannel linner. Margit had the blankets ticht up roon his chin, an' boys, the swite wis jist pinkin' aff o' 'im.

'It's broncaidis, Bob, broncaidis,' says Margit. 'Div ye hear yon sweevle at 'is breist? I dinna like the soon' o' yon sweevle. I'm tryin' t' swite it oot o' 'im, an' forbye, he likes a drappie toddy!'

The Turk seen tellt Margit that it wisna broncaidis, an' that fitivver micht be at Hector's briest, it wisna a sweevle.

'Did ye nae ging an' see the doctor fin I tellt ye, Hector?'

'No, Bob, I didna. I wis feart!'

'Did ye see the Witch-doctor droggist mannie instead?'

'Aye an' no, Bob, aye an' no!'

'Fit div ye mean, aye an' no?'

'Weel, Bob, last time I wisna richt I gid up t' see the Witch-doctor, an' he says 'Lat's hae a look at yer tongue!' Then he says, 'Oh gyaad, we're corkit, are we? We'll seen sort that!' An' he pits a sup stuff in a glaiss. 'Gladstone Road ye bide is't.' 'Oh aye!' So in goes a suppie mair stuff. 'Half-wye doon the street?' 'Aye'; so in goes a suppie mair. 'This side or yon side?' 'Oh, the far side'; a wee drappie mair. 'Tell me this noo; is yer closet at the mou' o' the close?' 'No, it's at the far end'; jist a wee skytie mair. 'Noo,' says he, 'drink that an' hame at yer hardest.' Man, Bob, yon mannie should nivver ha' been a droggist; he wid ha' made a richt architeck! I missed the seat by three inches! So, the day, fin I gid in, he says, 'Corkit again, are we?' I jist ran.

'Aye-aye, Hector,' says the Turk, lachin'. 'But ye'd better be serious. It's mair than time that something wis deen, but it's nae likely ye'll get the doctor the nicht; he's likely awa playin' gulf. Nivver aff the gulf-coorse.'

The Turk was really concerned about Hector's health. The pair shared a common birthday; they had been playmates in their childhood, and they had been shipmates all their years at sea. There was a deep, abiding friendship between them, and the fact that Margit and Hector were childless whereas Mary and Bob had 'a faimly like steppin'-steenies' was a source of continual, friendly banter.

'I doot it's the fire-engine for you, freen'!' says the Turk.

'The fire-engine?' says Margit. 'Fit wye could ye get a pair o' horse up this closie? There's jist nae room!'

'I'm nae spikkin' aboot that kine o' fire-engine!' says the Turk. 'I mean yon thing like a basin, wi' a rubber pipe an' soapy water.'

'Oh,' says Margit, 'That's fit they caa an enemy. I've seen een o' them!'

'Fit did ye say? An enemy? I wis thinkin' it wid be a first-class freen t' Hector if we could only lay hands on sic a thing! There's bound t' be een at the Fivver Hospital, but that's awa oot past Buchanhaven, hine ootside the toon. An' forbye, a boddy micht get the jandies usin' their een!'

'Jeemsie wid ken far t' get an enemy,' says Hector. 'Jeemsie kens aa mortal thing. I hear he's gaun wi' yon quinie that sings so bonny in the Mission choir.'

'The Mission! The Mission!' cries the Turk. 'Fit wye did I nae think o' that afore? They keep an enemy in the sick-bay, an' I'm sure Jim Forrest wid be willin' t' help. An' I'm sure he wid hae somebody that kens the wye t' work the thing. 'Plinty squeak, no plump.' Fit wye did ye nae mine on that, Hector?'

Here the Turk was recalling the words of a poor Dutchman, landed at the Blue Toon with severe abdominal pains, long, long ago. On that occasion the Mission's 'enemy' had proved a friend in need. To this very day, the famous words are an oft-repeated joke among East-coast fishermen.

Well, now, Jim Forrest who seldom got his proper title 'Superintendent', willingly obliged with both 'enemy' and personnel, and poor Hector was kindly and skilfully treated.

Monday morning saw the *Meadowsweet's* crew back on board preparing for sea. As Hector passed the galley door, he handed to Jeemsie the usual Gazette.

'Ye ken far t' pit that, my loon,' says he.

'My govies, Hector, ye're nae needin' that the day. There's a hale Gazette nae broken on, in aneth yer pilla!'

'Fine div I ken that, Jeemsie. Naebody kens that better than me. But ye see, my loon, there's fresher news in this een!'

That fairly put Jeemsie's pipe oot!

The Flooer o' Scotlan'

Once upon a time there stood on Keith Inch (the Queenie) a tall granite gable which, strictly speaking, was not really a gable at all since it formed the wedge-shaped corner where Ship Street meets Pleasure Walk. It was a man-made cliff of local granite, a noble prow defying the might of the North East gales which had vented their fury upon it over the long, long years.

In the distant days when I, like so many others, ran barefoot about that vicinity there was, set into the South wall of the old building, the Jawbone of a great whale. Even in those days the whale-bone showed signs of decay, and finally it rotted away completely, leaving in the wall a peculiar arched recess. This gave rise to the erroneous belief that, at some time the old, old building had been a Kirk. It was obvious, thought some, that a great arched window had been blocked up. Some window! Some Kirk!

There was however in the old edifice a special window, a tiny window, high-set in the lofty eastern corner, a proper eyrie affording an incomparable view over the North Sea. Any vessel bound for Peterhead from the Continent (and there were many), could be spotted from this look-out while still many miles off. Thus did the window become a favourite watch-tower for certain members of the pilotage fraternity.

In those days Peterhead had at least a dozen pilots who shared at least half-a-dozen boats, on whose bows the letter P was boldly displayed to indicate that this was an authorised Pilot-boat. Clinker-built, 25/35 feet in length, the boats were powered by petrol/paraffin engines, diesel engines being as yet unknown. None of the boaties had a wheelhouse; only a few had a stove whereon a kettle might be boiled, yet these small craft went several miles off to meet the incoming cargo-boats. I remember quite well how my father, who had the steam drifter, *Twinkling Star,* incurred the severe displeasure of the pilots by agreeing to tow the old 'scaffie' boat *Kitty* as far as Wick, so that her skipper, 'Slum' McLean could capture a prize. In Wick there was a great muckle 'saat-boat' landing a half cargo, the other half being for Peterhead. As soon as the steamer cleared the piers at Wick, Slum, the Peterhead pilot boarded her, and of course the steamer towed the *Kitty* home. On my father's return from a fortnight's line-fishing in Orkney waters, he was informed by the pilots that 'unfair competition' would not be tolerated. He never offended again.

The pilots themselves were local smaa-line fishermen, largely illiterate, and with never a ticket of any kind between them, but they knew their job. For many, many years they piloted safely into the port ships as big as any which enter the port nowadays, via an entrance much narrower than the present one. In their day, these old salts had two great disadvantages; there were no break-waters for the Bay, and steamers of that era had only half the propeller in the water when they had no cargo. This made them as easy to handle as recalcitrant barrage balloons.

Competition between these hardy seamen was very keen indeed. Since the rule was 'First alongside claims the ship', and since pilotage money was regarded as manna from Heaven, it was inevitable that the battle was largely a battle of wits, in which prior knowledge of a vessel's arrival could be of inestimable value.

Behold, now, therefore, at the lofty window on Keith Inch, three gallant shipmates, skipper and crew of the pilot-boat *Wildfire.* For hours they had kept watch on the distant horizon through a magnificent telescope which could not have come from anywhere else but the bridge of some great ship, wrecked on the Buchan coast. It was inconceivable that any or all of the trio could have purchased such a handsome instrument; fishermen of that time didn't earn such money. And, to be quite honest, the hale toon kent far the glaiss had come fae.

Now, in the clear, frosty dark of a spring evening the glaiss was being put to good use. The biggest saat-boat the toon would ever see was expected any time now. Wouldn't it be great if our three heroes could spot the ship before the 'opposition' did; and wouldn't it be even better if they could slip unobserved out of the harbour with maybe an hour's start?

At long last the skipper closed the great telescope and whispered, 'I see the ship, boys, I see the ship! I'd say she's aboot fifteen mile awa yet, but it's time we wisna here!'

So the trio rattled doon the aul widden stair an' oot onto the untarred road, where they soon realised jist hoo stiff they had gotten, wi' sittin' ower lang in the drauchty cock-laftie. So it was with a hopperty-kick kind o' gait that they made their way along the street, trying hard to hide their excitement.

In those days a great many people lived on Keith Inch; coopers, black-smiths, ship-wrights, and all the different tradesmen associated with a seaport. At the street corners little groups of men paced slowly back-and-fore, setting the world in order; here and there a few women-folk were 'hae'in a fine claik' afore they would bed the bairns that were still on the go. There was no shortage of bairns, for the 'Queenie Arabs' were a prolific race. So, jist for fear that some youngster might smell a rat and run ahead of them to tell the 'opposition' that the saat-boat had been sighted, our heroes took it canny for a bittie. Then, in the lower half of Castle Street they took to their heels and ran.

But, when they reached the corner, they jammed the brakes on. Disaster! Disaster! Their great head-start had been wiped out, for there, at the opposite side of the harbour several Leading Members of the Opposition were leisurely pacing to and fro beneath the gas lamp-post which stood on the dykie in Harbour Street, and whose base-bolts are still to the fore. Twa o' oor pals swore heartily; the third een didna sweer, cos he wis a dummy, but he made a few rather rude gestures in the direction of the enemy. It was impossible for the trio to reach their boat without being spotted, and that was the very last thing they wanted, for the head-start would immediately pass to the enemy. Granted, it would be only a few minutes, but minutes counted.

A council-of-war was imperative! Some great and wondrous plan was 'sair nott'.

'Noo, lads,' says the skipper. 'Hearken close! This is fit we'll dee. We canna see the boatie cos she's in the shadda o' the pier, but we ken exactly far she's lyin'. So we'll crawl agross the Brig – that's the easy bit. Then we'll ging doon on oor bellies an' sweem along the grun' like snakes, keepin' close t' the black stick so that yon mob winna see's. Mind ye, we'll need t' be gey quaet aboot it. Fin we come t' the first moorin' rope, we'll jist crawl across't, an' fin we're half-wye t' the neist rope we'll jist shiv oor legs ower the pier an' drap into the boat. It's high water, so we winna hae far t' drap! We can let the ropes go fae the boat, eence we get the engine started. C'mon, noo, hist ye clivver fast. We dinna hae aa nicht!'

Behold, now, in the shadows of the dimly-lit harbour, three peculiar figures sweemin' like ruptured partans along the black stick, that heavy, tarred, wooden kerb which surrounds the quay-edges in the Blue Toon, its original purpose being a stop against which one could back a horse and cart. Beneath the black stick there was a veritable treasure-trove of 'coal stew an' dried horse-dung', for hadn't the Cairnie discharged a cargo of coal into box cairts that very day?

For such a commando-like operation, worsit drawers and hairback breeks are not recommended, especially if they are accompanied by heavy jerseys, black silk mufflers and London House bonnets.

'For ony sake, dinna sneeze noo,' says the skipper. 'They're jist across the road! Nae far noo, lads; here's the starn rope.'

Inch by aromatic inch the three brave souls wormed their way to a position half-way to the next rope; then, on a silent signal from the skipper they 'shivved their legs ower the pier an' let go'.

Oh, boys, ye've nivver heard a soon like yon in aa yer days! Even the peer 'dummy' wis howlin', for the three o' them wis in the watter! The crafty enemy had shifted the boatie, leavin' the ropes in place.

'Boys!' says the Leader of the Opposition, 'It wid appear that the *Wildfire's* crew's takkin' a bath afore they ging oot t' the saat-boat. Seein' that we're nae jist so parteeclar, we'll tak' on the jobbie oorsel's. G'waa an' get the engine started!'

Oh, Flooer o' Scotland, when will we see your like again?

The Hallelujah Lobby

In the dim and distant past, say a couple of hundred years ago, the fair town of Peterhead was renowned as a spa. At the foot of Jamaica Street, among the rocks of the fore-shore, there was a spring whose waters were really famous for their health-giving powers. Over and around this spring a sturdy granite hoosie with a beautifully slated roof was built, access to its low, wide door being via a steep, stone flight of steps from the roadway above. The spring itself was known as the 'Wine Waal', probably a corruption of the title 'Wynd Waal', for at that time, Jamaica Street was simply one of the many wynds in the town. It is worth noting that, in this airt, the 'd' of 'wynd' is always silent. Indeed, I have never heard the word used in any other form apart from 'a wynie'.

Be that as it may, gentry from far and near flocked to enjoy the waters of the waal, and this necessitated the building of a commodious inn nearby. The inn was quite an imposing building, with roomy stables and out-houses for the horses and carriages of the guests. There was also a considerable annexe for any overflow of gentry, an annexe which was seldom empty.

As time went by, the gentry forsook the Wine Waal and sought fresh pastures. The inn gradually degenerated into a kind of slum, known in my youth as The Hallelujah Lobby, wherein an incredible number of folk had their abode. Since one room, or, at the most, two rooms were considered ample accommodation for a family, the in-habitants of the old building were as the sands of the sea-shore. So I thought! There were carters and tinkers, slaters and scaffies, and all sorts of folk housed under the old roof, for the most part decent, hard-working, honest boddies that couldna get a hoose onywye else, for council houses were as yet unknown.

I remember very clearly one particular old lady who rejoiced in the name 'Pots an' Pans', a name perfectly descriptive of her trade, for she was an itinerant seller of tin kettles etc. So good was she at her job, that certain makers of tay-pots and roosers in the city of Aiberdeen came to the Blue Toon to try to enlist her services. Alas, the old dear was rather fond of gin, and, in those days when it was quite permissible for a boddie's doorstep to project half across the pavement, she was very often in a horizontal position, with her birn of tin-ware rattling aboot her lugs! Many a time have I helped her to her feet!

In the thirties, the Hallelujah Lobby was demolished, most of the tenants being re-housed in substantial Council houses in a brand new scheme which, until street names were introduced, was never known as anything else but Dartmoor, altho' its official title was Ugie Park. About the same time, the Close Brethren built a Hall in Skelton Street, and I can recall very clearly that one of their number was not amused when I suggested that 'They kent fit they were deein', biggin' their hallie wi' Hallelujah steens!'

The site of the Hallelujah Lobby is now occupied by a very substantial block of Council flats. But fit aboot the Waal? Well, now, the Waal's still there! Jist across the road, in aneth the car park, the granite walls of the hoosie remain, as does the Waal itself. Mind you, I wouldn't advise anybody to drink of the waters. Not now!

The old building stubbornly resisted the efforts of the demolition squad, who thought they could easily tear the place to bits simply by hitching a laden motor lorry to a stout wire rope fastened to a high point near the roof. The solid granite walls just laughed at the puny efforts of the lorries, and not until a couple of steam traction engines took over, was any progress made.

Then the bairns moved in! On the scran for firewood! Sticks were a great prize! I can tell you that 60 or 80 bairns can shift a fantastic amount of timmer in a very short time. And the noise! Really unbelievable, till there came a sudden hush. As one old lady said, 'Fin I heard the quaetness, I kent there wis a vrangness!'

The bobbies had made a pincer movement and had the bairns trapped. But three bobbies, complete with breeches and puttees, could have the upper hand only for a short time; the youngsters eventually won the war!

Many years later, in a doctor's waiting-room, I got newsin' wi' an aal freen, a former tenant of the annexe portion of the Hallelujah Lobby. It was my question, 'Foo are ye likin' yer new hoose?' that set the ball rolling, and soon we were deep in reminiscences of the old place.

This Mrs Buchan (one of the many), told me how she, along with her man and three bairns, not counting another on the way, were housed in one single room. There was no water in the place, and the outside privy was about 100 yards away. Dr Taylor had been called to attend to one of the bairns that was gey sair made wi' the 'kinkhoast' (whooping cough) and, during his visit, he remarked that the family were in dire need of more commodious quarters. Even one more room would make a tremendous difference!

'There's nae hope o' that, Doctor!' says she. 'There's jist nae hooses t' be gotten naewye!' Then, rather sadly, she said, 'There is a room jist throwe the waa, but naebody 'll bide in't, cos somebody wis murdered in't lang ago. They tell me the bleed's still on the fleer! A great loch o't, at that!'

Dr Taylor made immediate inquiries as to where he might obtain the key to the 'lockit room' and, having found it in a solicitor's office, he threw the door wide open. The room was quite spacious and in perfect order, but, in the corner by the window, the floor-boards bore a dark, ominous stain! Bleed, boys, bleed!

Mrs Buchan refused to enter, but the doctor hastened to examine the grisly mark. 'Fetch your sweeping-brush!' says he. 'We'd better hae a richt look at this!'

With the surface dust removed, the great stain looked even uglier. A repulsive blotch of dark, reddish brown, with fainter markings around the edges.

'Nivver mind, Doctor!' says Mrs Buchan from the doorway. 'I couldna bide far there's been a murder!'

'M'lady!' says Dr Taylor. 'Ye've gotten an extry room noo! This is nae bleed ava! It's bark fae a herrin' net! Somebody, at some time laid a new-barkit net there. Look at the marks o' the meshes roon the edges! A gweed scrub, m'lady, an' Bob's yer uncle!'

Thus did that family acquire their 'more commodious

quarters', which they enjoyed for a further three years before being allocated a new hoose.

Surely it is not surprising that, on being informed of her good fortune. 'M'lady' simply said 'Hallelujah!'

Eyes and No Eyes

Long, long ago, although it seems but yesterday, I read my first detective story in our 'reading book' at school. If memory does not fail me, the book was the *Prince* reader, and the story centred on a young lad who went to visit his Grandad (on foot, of course). It transpired that Grandad, from a mere glance at the youngster, could tell the exact route taken by his visitor. Well, you see, there was the red hawthorn in the boy's buttonhole, there was a special type of clay on his shoes, and there were certain other little odds and sods which I have long forgotten. All combined to give the old man an accurate picture of the lad's journey, so much so that the boy was certain that Grandad had been watching him all the time.

The story, 'Eyes and no eyes', was a great favourite of mine for some time, but, as the years passed, it disappeared beneath a welter of more important things. As the Apostle says, 'When I was a child I spake as a child, I thought as a child, I understood as a child: but when I became a man, I put away childish things'. So the story wasn't lost; it was simply stored away in some secret place in the mind, ready for instant recall on some suitable occasion. It was actually 35 years later that Memory laid the old tale before me, fresh as on the day I first read it.

I had 'swallowed the anchor' (left the sea for life ashore), and now I was a sales rep with an oil firm, the contact between the office and some 600 customers, most of whom were farmers. Thus did I come to know the country roads like the back of my hand, and the country folk only a fraction less closely.

One of my first tasks was to introduce myself to my customers, and in so doing, I met some wonderful people, rich and poor, high and low and, in the process, I learned a great deal. Several of my former prejudices went by the board!

One of the names on my long, long list was that of J. R.

Allan, Little Ardo, Methlick. The name seemed to ring a bell in my mind, and I wondered if this could be the man whose writings I had enjoyed so often in the P&J on a Saturday. If this was the case, I wanted to meet him, customer or not, so I made for the farm.

'Oh, aye!' says the grieve. 'He fairly dis a lot o' writin'. Ye've come t' the richt place, but if it's himsel' that ye're seekin', dinna ging t' the back door, cos he'll be at the front, an' he winna hear ye. Ye'd better try the front door first!'

This was something new, for I had already learned that only a very few of the fairmer folk ever used their front door. It's probable that for weddings and funerals the front door is used, but for all other occasions, the back door is the entrance/exit. To be quite honest, I'm only assuming that the front door exists, for in all the thousands of calls which I made over the years, I never saw such a thing. Towns folk in general, and fisher folk in particular, set great store by the appearance of their front entrance; not so, the fairmers.

Behold me therefore, all dressed up for the occasion, knocking in vain at the front door, and about to leave the place when a voice cried 'Hey! I'm here!' There, at the far side of the lawn, on a rustic seat in a veritable sun-trap, the man I sought sat with a book in his hand. So I made my way across the grass. When I was within six feet of him, he brought me to a halt with the peculiar question, 'How long were you at sea?'

'Close on thirty 'ear!' says I. 'Is't my rolling gait that betrays me?'

'Nivver!' says he. 'Ye dinna hae a rolling gait, if sic a thing exists! I kent as seen as I saw ye, an' I've been sittin' here this meenit or twa, winnerin' fit on earth a man fae the sea 's deein' at my door!'

'Aha!' says I. 'Somebody must ha' tellt ye I wis comin'!'

'Not at all!' says he. 'Man, div ye nae ken that saat water's written aa ower ye? Ye couldna possibly hide it, even if ye tried!'

I stood for a moment in silent disbelief then he fired another question.

'Far div ye come fae?'

'Peterheid!'

'Oh aye!' says he. 'The Blue Toon! Born an' brocht up there, wis ye?' I nodded my head and started to speak, but again he silenced me.

'It's ten to one ye're a Buchan!' and when I nodded an affirmative, he smiled. 'That was easy! But there's a something aboot ye that still puzzles me!'

I decided to remain silent while he tried to solve the mystery.

'Yer father a Peterheid man?'

'Oh aye! Actually born in Burnhaven, but in Peterheid maist o' his days!'

'Burnhaven's near aneuch!' says he. 'I ken far Burn-haven is!' Then to my amazement, he came with some-thing which was half statement and half question, 'Yer mither's nae fae Peterheid'.

'Ye're richt, freen! She's fae Stirlingshire!'

'Ye're like yer mither's folk!' says he, as if suddenly enlightened.

'Richt again!' says I. 'I'm like my mither's folk!'

'I micht ha' kent!' says he. 'Ye dinna hae an Aiberdeen-shire face!' He was delighted that he had discovered the 'something aboot me' which had baffled him for a wee whilie. I was simply amazed, and somewhat amused.

On the way home that day, I suddenly recalled the story of 'Eyes and no eyes'. True enough, some folk have 'em, some folk don't! I'm one of the Don'ts.

Strange as it may seem, less than a week later, I had an almost identical experience at the farm of Andrewsford, near Fyvie, only this time there was no mention of the Aiberdeenshire face. I am still at a loss as to what an Aiberdeenshire face is supposed to look like. The lady of the house at Andrewsford managed to read me without touching on that aspect of the matter.

But, ever since these two instances, I have been espe-cially struck by the words of a certain woman of Samaria, when she said to her fellow villagers, 'Come, see a man, who told me all things that ever I did'. (John 4:29.)

Hill Silver

'Od, Peter!' says Mains. 'I didna expect t' see you here the day! Nae wi' aa this snaa! Ye should hae mair sense than come awa up here among the hills, in wither like this!'

'If I'd kent fit like it wis, I widna been here ava!' says I. 'But there's nae snaa doon at the coast. It's only in the last half 'oor that there's been ony t' speak aboot. Ye'll hae t' flit, Mains. Flit!'

'Aye, fairly!' says he. 'We'll think aboot flittin' eence we've heen oor tay! Snaa or oan snaa, ye fairly ken the wye t' judge fan the kettle 'll be bilin'. Come awa inside an' gie's yer crack, syne I'll lat ye see my new bull!'

'Oh!' says I. 'We've a new bull, hiv we? Fit is she; Charlie, or Hereford or Friesian? An' fit colour is she?'

Boys, I thocht he wid choke! He could hardly tak' 'is tay for lachin'.

'A bull's nae a she! It's a he, ye great goat! It's a bull, nae a boat!'

'Oh!' says I. 'Ye're aye learnin'.' I dinna like bulls!

Oot in the byre, he lat me see the great beast; black an' fite. Very near a ton, I wis thinkin'; an' I wisna far oot!

'She's a topper!' says I. 'A topper! But div ye nae think she wid be better wi' a stronger moorin' rope? That tow widna hang a cat!'

He wis away again, lachin'. 'That's a quaet beast,' says he 'Else he wid be bun' wi a chain! But I ken the tow's fair deen, an' the spare that I hae is jist as bad! Div ye think ye could mak' a halter? I canna dee a thing wi' tows!'

'Nae bother ava!' says I. 'I've a fine tow oot in the van. Cut 'ee the iron ring aff o' the spare halter, an' we'll hae a new moorin' rope in a meenit or twa!'

As I spliced the bonny new rope, Mains stood in admiration. 'Hey!' says he. 'Is there onything ye canna dee? I'm jist thinkin' ye could be a great help t' me!'

'Look!' says I. 'Dinna get nae fancy ideas. I'm willin' t' splice a halter for the bull, but I'm nae takkin' on t' mak brazeers for yer coos!'

He wis away again, lachin'. Then, when he'd gotten 'is breath back, he says, 'I've some idder thing t' lat ye see! C'mon!'

The 'some idder thing' was a snowdrift between a long, heavy iron roller and the garden dyke; say eight feet long and more than two feet deep.

'Look at the like o' that!' says Mains.

'Bonny fite snaa',' says I. 'Is that fit I'm supposed t' look at?'

'Wheesht! Jist wyte a meenit!' says he. Then, with a pick-axe shaft, he gently broke the frosted crust of the drift before scooping away some of the snow with his hands. 'Look at the like o' that, noo!' says he.

'That' was a beautiful salmon, gleaming silver in the sun. 'Look at the like o' that, noo!' says he, with a note of pride in his voice. 'There's anither five-and-twenty forbyes that een! You that kens folk that handles fish, could ye dee onything wi' that lot? Div ye think ye could sell them, somewye?'

'Far on earth did ye get that?' says I, astonished beyond measure. 'Ye're at least three mile fae the river, an' close on thirty mile fae the sea. I hardly think ye shot them doon fin they were fleein' ower yer heid, so, far did ye get them? An' dinna gie me nae lees!'

'I got them at the boddim o' my neep park!' says Mains. 'Doon in the howe there, atween the twa parks. There eesed t' be a burn there, although it's little mair than a ditch noo! But, man, the salmon still comes up at their appointed time, though fyles there's barely eneuch watter t' cover them. I can ging doon at nicht wi' a torch an' a big heuk, an' jist trail them oot! Nae bother ava! I'm fair scunnert aitin' the things noo, an' so's my neepers! Fit aboot it noo? I'll gie ye half o' the siller, if ye sell them!'

'Ye've been gey greedy, freen!' says I. 'Killin' aa yon fish, an' you nae needin' them! An' fit wye wid ee ken foo muckle siller I got for them, supposin' I sellt them?'

'I ken ye're nae gweed!' says he. 'But I dinna think ye'd chate me!'

'Will ye pey the fine if I'm catched?' says I.

'Ye're surely nae feart, are ye? Faa wid look for salmon in an ile van? An' specially your van, cos aabody kens ye'd nivver dee sic a thing!'

'See a hud o' a score o' the brutes!' says I. 'I'll tak a chance!'

I was just at the end of Main's road when I had to give way to a huge lorry, grinding up the brae. Then, sink me if he didna stop his lorry richt across my bows so that I couldna win oot!

'Aha!' thinks I. 'This lad's surely clean tint; I'll need t' tell 'im far he is!' So I oot-ower t' speak t' the chiel, but I met 'im at the front o's larry.

'Are ye lost?' says I.

'Lost?' says he. 'Nivver! I bide nae far fae here! I wis jist winnerin' if ye could be deein' wi' a lettrick bathroom heater. Spleet new! Fower fitt lang! Nivver oot o' the box! Guaranteed t' stite back! Thirty bob!' And he opened the passenger door of his vehicle to show me an array of heaters packed tightly between the door and the engine.

'The love o' Dod Vricht!' says I. 'Far did ye get that lot?'

'M.Y.O.D.B.' says he.

'Please yersel!' says I. 'But I'm nae needin' a bathroom heater, an' a thing's nae a bargain if ye're nae needin't! Could ye be deein' wi' a salmon?' And I opened the door of my van. Boys! His e'en near fell oot o's heid.

'&%ƒ&%ƒ' says he. 'Far on earth did ye get that lot?'

'Same place as you got yer heaters!' says I.

'Od!' says he. 'I'm aafa fond o' salmon, but I've aafa little siller! Fit wid ye be needin' for that big een?'

'Fower heaters, my loon. Chaip at half the price!'

The deal was done on the spot!

Well, now, Hilly took een, Bogs took anither, an' Dockens took twa. I'm tellin' ye, there wisna mony left b' the time I made the Blue Toon, far I got twa boxes o' kippers fae a smoker, an' a hale coil o' rope fae a chandler chiel. Nae scruples ava, yon cove! It wis a raivelt coil he gied me! I got ither odds-an'-sods forbye. Nae a bad day's work!

Neist day, Mains an' me sattled up. We pairted the siller, up an' doon the middle, as had been the deal. I nivver tellt 'im aboot the ten bags o' tatties, cos Mains had plenty tatties o' his ain! Mrs Mains wis aafa fine shuited.

Salted codlings drying in the sun and wind of summer. Basic ingredient of 'hairy tatties' in the winter. (1988)

Hielan' Briggie, Kinlochbervie.
N. Ritchie, Macduff.

*The old days were
not all good.*
N. Ritchie, Macduff.

'Jist the verra dunt for mairridge presents, yon bath-room heaters!'

Mains himsel' wis fine pleased.

'Ye're a great lad!' says he. 'I wis feart the fish wid ging rotten!'

'That mines me!' says I. 'I'll tak' the rest o' them awa, noo!'

'Och, ye're ower late, Peter! She's biled fit wis left, t' feed the hens!'

Od. I could ha' chappit the pair o' them!

'Hey, Peter!' cries he, as I started the engine. 'Fit on earth 'll I dee wi' yon great fyang o' tow that ye feess up?'

'Mak' brazeers t' yer blastit coos!' says I.

Hame-Made Wine

I was as green as girss, and the country folk kent, so they leuch at me. I was as fisher as a speldin, and the country folk kent that ana', so they leuch at me again. Nae a coorse lach, mind ye, but jist a quaet chuckle. To them I was something o' a ferlie, a rare bird, a stroonge chiel, for had I nae left the sea aifter near thirty 'ear at it? An' had I nae been a hale 'ear an 'uncertified' secondary school-teacher, an' had I nae turned doon a Fishery Officer's job, cos it meant leavin' hame? A chiel like that could hardly be normal, gaan aboot the country in a van, sellin' ile to fairmers. Some thocht he wisna jist the hale shillin'. They could ha' been richt!

Well, now, here was I, Traveller for an oil firm, serving the public, the all important link between Firm and Customer, the Sales Representative. Maybe I should tell you now that to fisher-folk sales-reps are jist 'traivellers', but to country-folk they are Travellers, with a capital T. Mony a time, ower the next eleven years, did I think I was jist lookin' for victims!

I must confess that my knowledge of things agricultural was absolutely minimal; I didna ken a bee fae a bull's fitt. My speech betrayed my fisher origin; the fact that I paced restlessly back-and-fore at the cattle Marts betrayed it even further, not that I sought at any time to hide it. But I was, after all, a stranger in a foreign land.

Then one fine day at Turra Mart, an aul, seasoned Traveller who aye wore a rose in his button-hole took me aside and gave me a great deal of sound advice which stood me in good stead over the years.

'Peter,' says he. 'Dinna look so worried! For a lang time, aabody 'll speak aboot ye, some 'll tak' the len o' ye, an' some micht even ging the linth o' bein' coorse t' ye. But jist ee keep a calm sough, an' aifter aboot three 'ear ye'll be accepted. Syne ye'll winner fit aa the t'dee wis aboot, an' ye'll hae the feelin' that a door's been opened! Till that time, jist sodjer on. Dinna pey ower muckle attention t' the fairmer; raither watch the wife, for if she likes ye, ye'll be their ile man nae maitter fit, He says. But if She disna like ye, ye needna bother. Nivver caa the fairm wife Mrs Fairmer unless ye're sure that she actually IS Mrs Fairmer, an' nivver refuse tay if ye're offered it.'

Jake wis richt wi' some things but, mind ye, a hantle o' the country-folk accepted me fae the start. A fyowe did tak' the len' o' me for a fylie until they realised that fyles I micht be takkin' the len' o' them. Thereafter we became good friends. I listened very closely, and soon acquired an extensive vocabulary of country terms so that I could converse quite knowledgeably about farm affairs. Since the Traveller is a welcome source of news to his clients, it's in his own interest to acquaint himself with local events, and with local 'claik' if necessary. I developed a deep thirst for knowledge and found that in this respect most folks were more than willing to help. Fun was inevitable, sometimes deliberate, sometimes quite spontaneous. Hard-workin', kindly folk, the country folk, roch an' ready at times, maybe, but aaricht at the hairt, an' maist o' them likit a lach.

Came the day I wis in the byre at Mains o' Currandad, speirin' the verra guts oot o' aul Sandy an' storin' aa the information in my heid. Fin it wis time t' ging hame, I said

I wis sorry for hinnerin' the wark, but he widna hear o' that.

'Peter,' says he, 'If ivver there's onything ye wid like t' ken, jist ee speir at me, for I ken ivvery mortal thing aboot fairmin'. It's fine t' see a lad so keen t' learn, an' ye've come t' the richt een. Fire aheid, ony time ye like!'

'Weel, Sandy,' says I, same's I wisna ower willin' t' annoy the man, 'Could ye tell me fit a "bugger" is?'

Od! I thocht for a meenit that he'd swallied 'is teeth, for he hoastit an' clochert an' spat, glowerin' into my face, same's he wis lookin' for something. But I had the curtains drawn, so he couldna see naething.

'Fit gars ye speir sic a thing?' says he.

'Weel,' says I, 'In the first fairm I wis in the day, the word apparently applied t' mysel'; in the neist place it seemed t' be a tractor that widna start; in the third place it wis his next-door neeper, an' noo, in your place it's a beast that's scourin'. Dis't mean different things in different places?'

Sandy keepit lookin', lookin'. I'm tellin' ye, I wis gey sair made! At last he got 'is breath back, then he says, 'As far as I can tell ye, it means a stick that the sawmill folk reject as nae bein' nae eese for naething'.

'Man, Sandy,' says I, 'That's jist gran'! A boddy's aye learnin'!' But I'm sure that fin aul Charlie Sim at Strichen used the word, he didna mean his timmer ava!'

Much of aul' Jake's advice proved very useful; some of it was utterly irrelevant, for every Traveller has his own individual approach, his own style and his own personality. You'll never find two alike, and exactly the same thing applies to his clients.

Well do I remember the day I went to see a dear old soul who was thinking she might replace her old coal-burning stove with the latest oil-burning type. She listened very closely while I extolled the virtues of the new appliance then, after a very short time for thought, she fired a proper bobby-dazzler at me.

'Will't burn a deid hen?'

'I doot hardly,' says I.

'Weel!' says she, 'I'm nae seekin't.'

On the same day, on the same errand I called at another farm about thirty miles distant. There I secured a firm order and enjoyed a fine cuppie o' tay wi' a Gaimrie Knottie then, while we sat newsin', I noticed, on the window-sill, three great muckle steen pigs (earthen-ware jars). The neck of each jar was tightly corked, and through the cork thre came a little glaiss tube, and on the end of the tube there was a little wee bottlie the size o' a matchbox.

'Fit on earth's that?' says I. 'Are ye a droggist in yer spare time, or are ye makkin' booms for the I.R.A.?'

'Oh!' says the fairmer, 'That's my outfit for makkin' hame-made wine! Wid ye like a glaiss?'

'No, thank ye,' says I. 'I nivver touch drink ava!'

'Och! That winna touch ye,' says he. 'It's jist a puckle rasps wi' a twa-three raisins throwe them. It's gran' stuff, tho' I say't mysel.'

Now, afore ye could say Jake, the deemie (she wisna Mrs Fairmer) had three glaisses on the table, filled fae a bottle that she took fae the press. I dinna think I ivver saw onybody move as fast.

Boys! Yon wis rare stuff! Jist like yon fruit cordial that the bairns get at Hogmanay. Smooth as velvet, an' nivver a sign o' a kick aboot it!

'Ye'll tak' anither drappie? says he.

'Aye, surely! That widna hurt a flee!' says I. An', as fast as lichtnin' the deemie had the glaisses fu' again. Great stuff!

But, half-wye throwe the second glaiss, the swaal seemed t' be risin'.

'Aha!' says I t' mysel', 'We're surely in for a coorse nicht. This swaal's the dog afore 'is maister.'

Things seemed to worsen very suddenly, and I could hear mysel' lachin' at naething. Nae a gweed sign! I'm gled I dinna drink, for I'm sure I wid mak' a richt feel drunk!

The deemie got baith her elbicks on the table an' reestit her heid on her hands. Then, lookin' me straicht in the face like a cockle-e'ed owl, she tellt me her name, her precise date of birth, foo muckle siller she had, coppers an' aa thegither, an' fit Bunk it wis in. Syne, stabbin' at her chest wi' her finger, she says, 'Ye'll need t' unnerstan' that I'm a Miss! I'm a Miss!'

'Aha!' says I in the profundity of my new-found wisdom. 'Ee'll be fit they caa a virgin, are ye?'

'Na! Nae yet!' she says.

Fortunately St Christopher whispered in my lug that it was time I was lookin' for Buchan Ness, so I left that port an' got onto the road. I was sure that the course for Buchan Ness was east-nord-east, but it's nae easy t' steer a course if somebody's stolen the compass. An' forbye, there wis solid rocks on baith sides o' me. (Actually they were dry-steen dykes). Now, ony feel kens that in such conditions the only sensible thing t' dee is t' drap the anchor, but it's nae easy t' drap the anchor if that's been stolen anaa! I couldna get the anchor naewye! So I jist stoppit the engine an' let her lie ower the broadside, like a trawler. Boys, what a nicht I put in. I sat for three strucken 'oors, grippin' onto the wheel, an' boys, she didna half roll! There wis a fylie that I thocht she wid ging richt ower on the tap o' me, but it's strange that she nivver took a drap o' watter.

At long last, jist afore dark, the wither eased awa an' I managed t' win hame.

'Faar on earth hiv ee been the day?' says her ain sel'. 'Ye look like a fish supper struck wi' lichtnin'. Ye hinna been drinkin', hiv ye?'

'Na, na!' says I. 'I've been awa seein' aboot a berth. I'm gaan back t' the sea the morn.'

'An' fit div ye think ye'll dee there, aifter aa this time ashore?'

'Och!' says I. 'I'll be aa richt. I'm gaan t' be skipper o' a rum-runner in the Virgin Islands.'

The Motor Bike

Once upon a time, some fifty-odd years ago, I had a cousin who had a thing about motor-bikes, just as today's youth has a thing about cars. Of course, in those days cars were very scarce indeed, for a car could cost as much as £350, and nobody had that sort of money. Not even all the Doctors had cars, some of them doing their rounds on a push-bike, with their bag slung from the handlebars. Anybody with a car was bound to be in the highest layer of Society, and even a boddy with a motor-bike and sidecar was doing very nicely, thank-you, in a world where most folk's transport was Shanks' mare.

Well now, into this world comes Cousin, all Oxford bags and Brylcreem. Oxford bags were trousers whose leg width was 22 inches, the very height of fashion at that time. They looked not too bad on a tall chap, but they did nothing for the average youth, especially when a following wind made them spread as wide as any skirt, giving the wearer the appearance of a tea-cosy with a figurine on top. Brylcreem was a pure white hair-dressing which was sold in jars and clarted on by the gallon. The rugged, windswept look was definitely not in fashion. I've heard that the mannie who invented the stuff made it in his sheddie, and made a million by selling the recipe to some international cosmetics firm.

Cousin was more or less a foreigner, for he came from the Central Belt, that indeterminate slice of Scotland somewhere south of Perth. He simply could not understand our language, but was agreeably surprised that we understood his. Well, you see, he was simply speaking the same tongue as our Mither spoke, so we had no difficulty with it. The main purpose of Cousin's visit was, apparently, 'to look for a job', for there were no jobs down south. He nottna come to the Blue Toon for a job, cos the queue of unemployed stretched from the Buroo, in Back Street right along Thistle Street and up Marischal Street as far as Marioni's. That was the time of the Great Depression, so Cousin didna get a job, but I dinna think he wis ower sair worried, as lang as he got his dole on Friday. I think it wis fourteen shillins he got. That's 70p in decimal coinage. . . . Not a lot.

But the outstanding thing about Cousin was his motor-bike, a great bummer o' a machine that had 'won the T.T. races in the Isle of Man last summer!' When I asked him how any young unemployed fella could afford such a machine, he said that only half the bike was his, a pal owning the other half. To raise the money, the pair shaved their heads, so that they couldn't go to the dancin', or the picters for fear of ridicule. 'We kept it up,' says he, 'for six months, and the money accumulated very fast. In fact, we lived like hermits!' Sadly, I doubted his word. Aff o' fourteen bob? Nivver! When I asked whether it was the front half or the rear half that was his, he wisna neen shuited!

Cousin was quite popular with the local girls, for he was an accomplished dancer who could charm a bird oot o' a tree. I know that some of the young ladies willingly 'peyed him in' to the dance, simply for the pleasure of his expertise and the benefit of his instruction. He could fairly dance! So it was tennis, dancin', and the motor-bike. 'Lookin' for a job,' he called it.

On the day prior to his departure for home, Cousin offered me a hurl on his machine. I was very nervous, but I didn't have the guts to refuse. He was delighted at my acceptance, and I'm sure he set out to repay me for the teasing to which I had subjected him, for the bike gid oot the Broch road like an evil speerit! Boys, I wis scared stiff! Parks o' corn and wheat, neeps and tatties and peys and barley gid bye like a great muckle pot o' broth. Ninety mile an hour, and still he wisna satisfied. We came hame by Longside, and we took the Flushing Straight at one hundred and forty.

My great mistake, born of inexperience, was to sit rigid, instead of leaning over with the machine as it took the various bends. I was actually fighting the machine and, by the time I got home, I wis like a vrung cloot. Since that day I personally have had a thing about motor-bikes! I widna ging on one o' them ... nae for a pension!

Cousin left for home next day, found a job, and eventually worked himself to the top, but not in Oxford bags, of course.

Every time I recall that hair-raising journey, I find myself in deep sympathy with the loon fae Foggieloan that had an experience similar to mine. This loon's big brither had gotten a great muckle two-stroke bike, an' widna rest until he got the loon on the pillion. But, before starting out, he did advise the youngster to lean with the machine. This would greatly help the driver to handle the powerful brute, and at the same time the passenger would have a more comfortable ride.

So it was off to Banff and a baggie o' chips. As they sat near the pier enjoying their snack, Big Brither says, 'Foo are ye likin' the hurl?'

'Fine!' says the loon. 'But it's aafa caal fin ye ging faist. The win' jist fussles throwe my claes, for I dinna hae a jacket on. It's maybe aa richt for you, wi' yer leather jacket, but I'm fair frozen!'

'Nivver mined aboot that!' was the reply. 'But jist wyte a meenit. I think there's a spare jacket in yon saddle-bag, jist far ye've been sittin'. Lat's hae a look!'

Sure enough, there was a spare leather jacket in the pannier, but it had one glaring fault ... it simply would not fasten at the front. Zip fastener broken beyond repair.

'Weel!' says Big Brither, 'Ye're as weel athoot it, if it disna fasten, for it'll jist blaa open like a sail. In fact, ye wid be blaan clean aff the seat. Fit are we gaan t' dee aboot that?'

'Hey!' says the loon, 'I could aye pit it on back-to-front. That wid surely keep the draacht oot! Fit div ye think?'

'Great idea! Jist gran'! Fit wye did I nae think o' that mysel'? Get the thing on, an' we'll gie't a try, onywye.'

So, on goes the jacket. Jist the job! The verra dunt!

'Noo than!' says Big Brither, 'A bittie o' binder twine roon yer middle, an' that's you riggit! The collar comes up as far as yer e'en ... Man, ye've a better rig than I hae mysel'!'

Oh, the loon was fair chuffed! Cosy as a flech on a sheep. Rarin' to go!

'Noo!' says Big Brither, 'I'll tak ye along the coast road as far as Pennan, syne we'll ging hame by Cyaak an' Byth an' the Mill o Pot. We'll maybe get a fly cup in Turra, forbye. It'll be a richt fine run on a bonny day like this.'

It wis a richt fine run! Yon loon could fairly lean ower wi' the bike, an' her gaan like a certain kind o' bee (ye ken the kind I mean). But, sad to say, somewye aboot the Barnyairds o' Delgaty the loon leaned a hackie ower far ower, an' fell clean aff the bike, in amon' the lang girss at the roadside. What a clyte! The bike wis near in Turra afore the loon wis missed, syne Big Brither came roarin' back to look for 'im.

He didna hae far to look, for three fairm chiels that had been at the hyowe were stannin' on the grass verge, lookin' doon at something.

'Is he aa richt?' cries Big Brither, pushin' in atween them. 'Is he aa richt?'

'Weel, noo!' was the reply. 'He wis spikkin' awa fine till we turned 'is heid the richt road!'

Gweed preserve us aa fae motor bikes.

Wheelies

As far as I could see, Gran had nae feet! Maybe her feet had been worn awa like the soles o' sheen, for Gran was a fearsome age. Even my ain feet grew sair at times, rinnin' aboot the rocks an' san' o' the foreshore, so maybe that was the trouble wi' Gran's feet ... she had played ower muckle doon the braes, an' worn her feet aff! Peer aal wifie! She was even a lot aaler than Ma, an' Ma was an aal wifie hersel', but I kent that Ma had feet, cos I could see them! So, fit wye could Gran ging aboot the close an' the green athoot feet? Wheelies! It couldna be naething else but wheelies aneth yon lang skirts, skirts that brushed the grass, an' nae doot she wore skirts that linth to hide the wheelies. That was it, for sure!

Came the time when Gran had to 'ging an' lie doon, cos she wis nae weel!' For a long, long time she lay in her feather bed in an upstairs bedroom where I visited her daily, being the only grandchild permitted to enter the room. I was sorry for the peer aal wifie, cos she lay there singin', 'Bring forth the royal diadem, and crown Him Lord of all!' She wis surely dottled, for there wisna sic a word as 'diadem'; 'Diamond', maybe, but nivver 'diadem!' On very rare occasions, I got a puff cracknel wi' butter on't fae Gran, cos she couldna manage it hersel' and, wi' the titbit in my hand, I would run outside to arouse bitter jealousy in the hearts of my playmates. Puff cracknels? My govies!

Then, one day, Gran passed away. I didna greet, cos Gran wis awa t' the Happy Land t' see Jesus. I was a bittie puzzled at this, cos Gran was in a great, lang box, ben in the Room, wearin' a bonny fite goon! Deydie sat dressed at the heid o' the box, unveiling Gran's countenance to each one of the innumerable callers, who gied their e'en a dicht sayin, 'She's richt like hersel', isn't she?' That, too, puzzled me! Faa else could she be like? When Deydie lifted me up to see my Gran, I thocht she was jist like Gran, but my swift glance left me still wondering whether it was feet or wheelies that she had, for I couldn't see!

This, at a very tender age, was my first sight of Death. I was far too young to have the slightest idea what it meant! But I wasn't too young to remember! On a brass plate on the lid of the box, propped against the wall, I saw a 7 and a 2 beside Gran's name. I didna ken that the figures meant 72. I jist kent that they meant 'aafa, aafa aal!' I dinna think that noo! 'When I was a child, I understood as a child.'

Isn't it passing strange how Memory, from the secret depths of some magical filing system can, quite unbidden, bring long forgotten things to life, to present them to us clear and fresh as on the day they happened? Wordsworth says 'They flash upon the inward eye, which is the bliss of solitude'. Remember that line? Well do I know about the inward eye, for it has brought me many a sharp reproof in the midnight watches. . . . 'Fit are ye lyin' there lachin' at, ye great feel?' And, somehow, it is beyond me to explain!

Fit aboot the day that Untie Jean wis byaakin' breid, as she so often did, breid being oatcakes and bread being simply loaf. Some cousins of mine from a distant shire had come to visit Gran, while some local cousins had come to see the strangers, and I, not to be outdone had come to see them all. The room was grossly overcrowded, and unbearably hot, but on such a day of torrential rain it wasn't possible to play outside. So we watched the baking process with great interest for a whilie.

Jean rolled the mixture into a flat disc before transferring it to the iron 'girdle', whereon it was baked for a whilie above the fire. When the consistency of the disc was deemed to be just right, it was cut into 'corters' (triangular quarters), which were browned before the glowing coals. In this final browning process, the corters assumed a beautifully curved form, not at all flat. With syrup or treacle, they were delicious, a temptation to hungry bairns. And that's where the trouble started! Some of us kept nippin' at the fresh breid, incurring the displeasure of Gran, who stood at the table in a supervisory role only. She kent better than to interfere wi' Jean, but she fairly managed to control us bairns.

'G'waa an' play ootside!' Then, seeing the heavy rain, 'Bide awa fae the table, an' bide awa fae the fire! G'waa an' play hide-an'-seek or something!'

So, hide-an'-seek it was, and I was to be 'the mannie'. I

had to turn my back, steek my e'en and say, 'Five, ten; double ten; five, ten a hunder!' Nae ower fast ye ken, so that the ithers wid get time to hide.

Well, now, gettin' them wis jist nae bother ava! Far could they hide, onywye? But there was one cousin who had me beat! Search as I might, I jist couldna get him, and I was on the verge of cryin' 'I'm bate!' when there came a sudden movement of Gran's skirt, the skirt that brushed the fleer. Up came the hem, and oot popped the culprit whom I grabbed in glee.

'Got ye! Got ye!' says I, in triumph.

'Aye, maybe!' says he, in a surly tone. 'But ye widna gotten me yet, if Gran hidna fartit!'

Boys, I've jist mined this meenit! I should ha' speired at him if it wis wheelies or feet that she had! Still, maybe it wis ower dark t' see!

NOTE   Several women in the town baked 'breid' for the drifters, and every one was extremely jealous of her good name as a baker. Normal practice was for the skipper to order the breid from the ship's grocer, always stipulating who should do the baking. The grocer would then deliver the oatmeal to the required address, and uplift the finished product in due time.

For baking 5 stone (32 kilos) of meal, using her own fire, the baker was paid £1.

The Nightcap

For more than fifty years Dod and Weelim had been close friends. They were actually distant cousins of a sort and, all their working days, they had never known anything but the sea. Year after year they had followed the herring shoals, and they kent every hole and bore from Yarmouth north-about to Milford Haven, including the Shetlands. But now advancing years had decreed that they should forsake the big boats for a ripper boatie, so their livelihood was now derived from codlings, mackerel and lobsters.

'Nae muckle siller ava!' says Dod. 'Jist as muckle as mak' it interestin'.'

Fishermen of the old school, the two confirmed bachelors lived in simple style, each in his own little cottage in a village on the Buchan coast. The cottages themselves had been handed down through several generations but, since Dod and Weelim seemed to be the last of their line, speculation was rife as to who would inherit the hoosies. Village claik! Ye ken the wye o't.

Only for weddings or funerals would the pair don collar and tie, the only difference between the two events being that a funeral required a black bonnet. The normal go-ashore rig for Dod and Weelim comprised a navy blue serge jacket, a home-knitted jersey (also navy blue) and a pair of tailor made 'hairback' (Kersey) trousers almost black in colour. The bonnet for such an outfit was invariably checked, and cost at most half-a-crown.

Now, should you query the colour of the trousers, let me tell you that the colour varied from village to village. Lesser breeds might wear navy blue, or a deep, deep shade of brown, but the garments would all be of top grade cloth and, more often than not, they would be bought 'on tick'.

Was there nothing, then, to distinguish our heroes from the common rabble? Aye, surely, there was a something! They did the Pools!

'The Pools?' says you. 'Nivver! I'm jist nae for that ava!'

'Ah, but aye,' says I. 'They did dee the Pools on the quiet!'

In fact, Dod and Weelim had been committing this cardinal sin for years. When first they set foot on the slippery slope, Dod says to Weelim, 'We'd better keep this unanimous!'

'Ye mean anonymous!' says Weelim.

'I dinna mean onything o' the kind!' says Dod. 'I mean that naebody has to ken aboot it, cos if this village comes to hear aboot iss, we'll be putten oot!'

'Ye're richt there, freen!' says Weelim. 'Unanimous it is!'

What a stammagaster they got when, after twenty-odd years, they were informed that they had won the jackpot of some £60,000 between them. (That was a lot o' candy, in those days). If they would care to come to London for the Presentation, they would be met at King's Cross and everything would be laid on. They would certainly appear on Pathe-news in the picters, and it was possible that they just might get a mention on the wireless.

'We'd better ging,' says Weelim. 'I'm black affrontit! Lat's get oot o' here afore we're yokit on. Fit wid my peer aal mither say?'

'I've haard ye at that afore!' says Dod. 'Jist mine fit yer aal mither said afore she deet.... "If ivver ye look at a wumman, Weelim, I'll turn in my grave!" They tell me the cemetery mannie caas her Furlin' Jess. Ha-ha! Ye rascal. C'mon, lat's tak the train.'

So the prizewinners hurriedly packed their cases and swyted their wye sooth, to be met, as promised, by a Pools mannie who immediately took charge of them.

The hotel manager gave the two unaccustomed guests a warm welcome, and appointed an underling to see to their every need.

'This way, gentlemen', says the mannie. 'I'll show you to your rooms.'

'Rooms!' says Dod. 'Rooms! There's jist the twa o's. Surely ae room's eneuch!'

'Just as you wish, sir. That can quite easily be arranged.' So, after a short confab with the receptionist, he led the way to the lift, carrying the two battered old cases, neither of which could possibly be locked, for the keys had disappeared some time after the Boer war.

'Isn't iss bonny, noo?' says Dod on seeing the room.

'Richt bonny!' says Weelim. 'An' the water closet's jist ben the hoose. Boys, that's the first water closet I've seen wi' a bath in't. I'll maybe wash my feet the nicht.'

'They're nae oot o' the need o't, aswarn!' says Dod. Then to the mannie, 'Is there some ither body sleepin' here the nicht?'

'Not at all, sir, not at all! Why do you ask such a thing?'

'Weel!' says Dod, 'There's twa bides.... There's surely little need for that, fin there's jist the pair o's.'

'Sir!' says the mannie, whose mither had been a rovin' kind o' quine fae The Gash, and had bestowed upon her offspring the gift of tongues that they might comprehend the Buchan Doric. 'Sir, when one is in London, one sleeps in separate beds. That's why there are two.'

'I'd fairly like to see that,' says Weelim. 'A boddy wid need to be haavert to dee that!'

The mannie gied Weelim a queer look before announcing, 'Dinner is at eight, gentlemen. You'll have time to wash and brush up before then. Now, should you require my services later in the evening, just pull gently on this bell-cord, and I'll be with you immediately. Don't hesitate to use it', indicating the ornate tasselled cord which hung in a corner. 'I trust you will enjoy your meal.'

Some twenty minutes later, despite the extensive and elaborate menu in the dining-room, the perplexed Chef was confronted with a special order for 'mince an' tatties for two, wi' twenty-meenit sweemers (dough-balls)'. It says a great deal for the Chef that he keepit the heid and coped magnificently, earning the profuse compliments of the two diners (foreigners, of course). Well, how was he, a Sassenach, to know what 'the verra dunt' meant?

Such were the amenities of the hotel that our heroes nivver socht ootside and, replete with their late dinner, they would turn in rather earlier than usual. After all, it had been a long, hot, tiring day, and they were no longer in their pottystatur (prime of life). But a tremendous shock awaited them in their room, for their mannie had been rakin in their cases and, on finding no pyjamas, had managed to produce a couple of sets from the hotel's glory hole.

'Dalmichty!' says Weelim. 'Fit's iss noo? A suit o' claes? Iss 'll be to wear at the presentation the morn. We're gey weel aff, gettin' claes an' baabees anaa!'

Dod was a wee bittie suspicious. His only experience of sleeping in strange quarters had been the time when he had been obliged to spend a week in the Church of Scotland Hostel in Yarmouth with a touch of flu. The two nurses had his linner (flannel sark) and his worsit draars aff afore he could wink, and had had him robed in a royal blue nightie. For a hale week he had felt utterly naked.

Nor would he ever forget a hardy skipper who defied all efforts by the nurses to remove his shocking-pink, bullet-proof nether garments. A bonny ticket he was too, in royal blue and pink! This same skipper had the disconcerting habit of rudely interrupting any conversation with the observation, 'Prayer changes things!' So fed up did Sister MacArthur become with this annoying conduct that one day she retorted, 'Skipper, if I thocht that prayer would get the drawers aff ye, I would pray very hard indeed!' He never annoyed her again.

As I said, Dod was suspicious. 'We'd better tit the towie (pull the cord) an' see fit the mannie says.' The mannie duly answered the signal and explained that the garments were not for the presentation ceremony, but were merely what Londoners called 'night attire', and the gentlemen would be expected to sleep in them.

'Oh!' says Dod. 'Good grief!' says Weelim.

Scarcely had the mannie departed when Dod was tittin' the towie again.

'Div we wear this claes abeen wir draars or aneth them?'

Patient as ever, the mannie told them that 'in London one does not sleep in one's drawers; one takes them off!'

'Oh!' says Weelim. 'Nivver!' says Dod. A few minutes later, Weelim was heard to mutter, 'Time the missionaries wis here, sinn! Fancy sleepin' wi' yer draars aff!'

In a strange bed, in strange clothing, our friends found sleep very elusive. Then, suddenly, Dod remarked, 'Hey, Weelim, there's a thing aneth your bide something like the flooer-pot that oor Isie keeps her aspidistra in. But this een has a hannle, so it canna be a flooer-pot, an' that's nae a place for a flooer-pot onywye!'

'Strange!' says Weelim. 'I'm jist lookin' at a thing like that aneth YOUR bide. Will I tit the towie an' see fit iss is for?

'It's gey late, but go aheid an' see fit he says.'

The mannie wisna neen suited, and spoke kind o' sharp. 'That, gentlemen, is what we in London call a nightcap. Goodnight!'

'We're surely nae richt riggit yet!' says Dod. 'Fit says we try the things on?'

Behold then our two pals, sartorially perfect and suitably helmeted, Dod pechin' an' tyaavin', nivver a wink; Weelim fast asleep.

Finally, in sheer exasperation, Dod reaches across an' shaks Weelim. 'Fit wye is't that ee can sleep wi that on yer heid, fin I canna get a wink ava?'

Only half awake, Weelim glowered oot aneth the brim o's nightcap and said. 'Hae a wee bittie o' sense, freen! Try turnin' the snoot to the front!'

The Presentation

At the first hint of daylight in the window, Dod was awake. He had discarded his 'nightcap' at midnight, restoring it to its rightful place under the bed, and promising himself that he would tell the mannie in the morning exactly what he thought of folks who, apparently, didna ken ony better than to wear a helmet in bed. But when, on the stroke of seven, the mannie arrived with a trolley bearing tea for two, Dod forgot what he had meant to say. Indeed, he didn't get time to say anything, for the mannie, on seeing the sleeping Weelim still resplendent in his helmet, had disappeared rather hurriedly with a few muttered words.

'Fit wizzat the mannie said eyvnoo?' says Weelim, coming to life.

'Something aboot a B.F. He surely kens aboot boats,' says Dod.

'He micht ha' said if there wis ony herrin' in the Broch the day,' says Weelim. Then, on spying the tay, 'Hame wis nivver like this! Still, mine ye, he micht ha' brocht a buttery cookie eence he wis on the pirr. Fit div we dee noo?'

'Bath!' says Dod. 'Bath! I hinna heen a bath since I was in the Navy, an' that wisna yesterday!'

'Weel! Ye'd better watch that the caddis (fluff) oot o' yer bellybutton disna choke the drain,' says Weelim, still resentful at Dod's remark of the previous evening about his feet.

Much later, the pair of them, cleaner and fresher than

for many a long day, sat down to breakfast, once more faced with an amazing choice of dishes.

'Hey!' says Dod, scanning the exotic menu, 'Wid yer hairt tak' a kipper?'

'Aye, surely! But ye'd better mak it twa!'

So kippers it was, and they were really delicious. If there was a 'mote in the meen', it was that they could hardly use their fingers on the kippers as they would certainly have done at home. It cannot be denied that the kipper is vastly improved by the use of one's fingers, which must be repeatedly licked. I'm sure that it's the licking that enhances the flavour, adding a touch of eastern promise. There was some discussion as to whether the kippers were of east or west coast origin, and there was some speculation on the method of fishing ... drift-net, ring-net or trawl.

'Speir at the mannie!' says Weelim.

'Far div ye get yer herrin' fae?' says Dod.

But the waiter was of little help, merely suggesting that they would probably have come from Billingsgate.

'Nivver seen that name on the chart!' says Dod. 'They're surely imported.'

Breakfast over, a Pools representative took our friends on a tour of the great city. This was their first hurl in a car, and they fairly enjoyed it.

'Iss maan be a fair toon!' says Weelim. 'Bigger nor Yarmooth, think ye?'

'Jist a thochtie, maybe,' says Dod.

Lunch was a protracted affair, very posh and proper. When Weelim expressed amazement at the 'great muckle latrines o' soup', Dod suggested quietly that he didna think that wis the richt word to use, tho' he wisna ower sure himsel' fit the richt word wis.

Then came the presentation, the long awaited moment. Both Pathe Gazette and Movietone News had cameras on the scene, so they would be on the picters sure enough. There were several Press photographers present, publicity being the order of the day, but there was an unexpected hitch when it came to the actual handing over of the money.

'Fit's iss?' says Dod. 'A bittie o' paper? A cheque, did ye say? We're nae for nae cheques. Nae fears! A boddy could loss a cheque in the train, or a boddy micht get it stealed. Ye'd better gie's the baabees; cash, so's we'll ken exactly foo we stan'.' And on this he was adamant. In vain did the Pools men plead with the pair that such an amount of cash could be 'stealed' far more readily than a cheque, and forbye, it would be difficult to obtain at such short notice.

'We'll wyte!' says Weelim. 'The train's nae till nicht.' And wyte they did.

So it came to pass, some two hours later, that our heroes found themselves on the pavement with their pooches fair stappit wi' siller (that includes oxter pooches). The Pools men had washed their hands of them, leaving them to their own devices.

'Fit 'll we dee noo?' says Dod. 'It's a fyle yet or train-time.'

'Weel,' says Weelim. 'It maan be near supper-time noo, but I canna say I'm on for muckle supper. Fit says we get a baggie o' chips?'

'Good idea!' says Dod. 'Jist the verra dunt.'

Behold the two tycoons now, sauntering along the pavement wi' a baggie o' chips apiece and licking their fingers in the approved fashion.

'Iss is the same kine o' chips that we eesed t' get fae the stallies in Yarmooth, lang an' fite but richt fine tasted. Ye mine yon stallies, Dod, far they sellt cockles an' mussels an' tripe an' trotters an' aa that kine o' trash! Did ivver ye try the tripe, freen?'

'Oh gyadd! Dinna pit me aff my chips. Ye'll hae me clean scunnert!"

Thus the desultory conversation as the pair wandered along, amazed at the great flow of traffic, both mechanical and human.

'A hantle o' fyolk! A gryte hantle o' fyolk!'

Very soon our heroes were completely lost, but Dod's mither wit led him to seek guidance from a taxi-driver who was momentarily without a fare.

'The Aberdeen train, mate? That'll be King's Cross, and you're miles away from that. But I can easily take you there, if you like.'

Dod explained how they had a couple of hours to spare, time which they didn't wish to waste in a railway station. Could the cabby suggest any alternative?

'Certainly!' says the cabby, with an eye for business. 'I know a nice place where you can watch a film for an hour or so. It's a foreign film about nudists!'

'Nudists?' says Weelim. 'Fit on earth's that?'

'Bare weemin!' says Dod. 'Bare weemin! Bare nyaakit weemin! I'm thinkin' we'd better nae tak' ye there, or yer peer aal mither 'll be licht-heidit furlin' in her grave! Is there nae some ither wye that ye can think o', driver?'

'Well,' says the cabby. 'There's the Motor Show, if you're interested in cars. I could take you there and wait for you while you browse around, then I'll take you to your train. How does that sound?'

'Couldna be better!' says Dod, but Weelim wasn't quite so keen.

'My legs is sair, an' we could hae a richt fine seat in the picters, supposin' the wifies is bare or no! I wid raither see the film.'

'Aswarn ye wid,' laughed Dod. 'But if they're foreign, ye widna ken a word they're sayin', an' I'm sure ye widna like that.'

Before Weelim could think of a suitable retort, he was bundled into the taxi, and they were off to the Motor Show.

'I wid fairly like to hae a car!' says Dod. 'I enjoyed yon hurl we got the day. It's putten a great idea into my heid, Weelim. We'll ging an' hae a lookie at ony rate. That winna cost muckle, I'm sure. An' for ony sake, dinna sit there glowerin' an' sulkin' like a bairn.'

Weelim had no interest whatsoever in things mechanical, but his half-neeper had been smitten hard by the car bug, so much so that he had conceived the idea that he 'micht ging hame in a car instead o' the train'. It never crossed his mind that some sort of training, however rudimentary, might be necessary.

The first thing to meet our friends' gaze as they entered the great hall, was a beautiful, gleaming monster in dark green livery. The bonnet seemed to be exceptionally long, and at the opposite end, as if to balance the front, the boot seemed to be just as long. The 'wheelhoose' was in the middle, and didn't amount to very much at all, since it was a two seater. There was no denying that she was a beauty, and the badge on the bonnet proclaimed her quality.

'Jist look at the like o' that, noo!' says Dod. 'Isn't 'at bonny noo? An' see the size o' the starn locker? Aswarn ye wid get twa boxes o' ripper codlins in there, nae bother ava!' Then, pointing to the bonnet, 'Weelim! Div ee see fit I see? That'll surely please ye, noo!'

'That' was a dainty little statuette in gleaming silver, some sort of nymph or goddess, apparently about to take flight from the cap of the radiator (far ye pour in the watter), and she was certainly in the altogether.

Weelim was most impressed!

As was to be expected, a keen young salesman, dressed like a circus horse and vringing his hands in anticipation, was immediately at hand.

'This is the finest car in the world, sir, without the slightest doubt!' But I'm sure there's little need for me to tell ye fit the mannie said; ye'll ken the blurb and the flannel which remain the same from age to age, no matter where. But listen to the chiel when he says, 'Sir will no doubt have noticed that this, the very latest model, is now fitted with a mechanical or electrical windscreen wiper!'

'Fit dis that mean?' says Weelim.

'It jist means,' says Dod, 'That there's nae fartin' aboot wi' a cloot fin it's rainin'. Great fit education can dee, intit?'

Dod had a lookie inower the car, then he tried to twang the spokes on the wheels (something like the wheels on a motor bike), as if they were a harp, then he says, aa at eence. 'Ziss motor for sale?'

'Most certainly, Sir!' says the salesman. Then, with a look of doubt at Dod's unsophisticated appearance, 'But she is rather expensive, Sir!'

'Nivver mine that!' says Dod. 'Jist say foo muckle siller ye're needin'.'

'I'm afraid, sir, she would set you back to the tune of three thousand pounds! But one must not forget that the figure quoted includes the starting handle which, in some lesser cars is classed as an extra.'

'Weel!' says Dod, producing a wad of notes near as big as a fish box, 'If that be the case, I'll tak' twa!'

I'm afraid my pen is entirely inadequate to describe the scene as Weelim, producing a similar wad, and shivvin' Dod oot o' the road, says

'Nae ower fast, freen. Nae ower fast! I'll pey for this lot! EE PEYED FOR THE CHIPS!'

Broken Biscuits

For Jinsie, it had been a long, hard day. Long before sunrise, she had spent a frustrating hour in the washin'-hoose, trying in vain to light the boiler fire with damp sticks. As a last resort, she had crossed the road to the stony beach, where she had found a few half-burnt splinters of wood among the ashes of a firie kindled by some bairns the night before. These had finally got the fire going, but the water in the boiler took a long time to heat, so Jinsie was well behind schedule when she roused her three quinies for their breakfast porridge. Normally, she would have been 'weel tee wi' the work', but this was to be 'een o' yon kine o' days!' She was quite sure of that!

As soon as the bairns were off to school, Jinsie was at the washin'-tub, scrubbing and scouring at the two shifts of heavy clothing sent home from Yarmouth by Jinsie's man and teenage son. This, on top of her washing for herself and the quines, was enough to give Jinsie a sair day's work. Hot water had to be taken from the boiler to the tub in a pail or a pannie, then the boiler had to be topped up. The fire also required stoking from time to time. Every article had to be hand scrubbed, then thoroughly rinsed before being taken throught the great, murderous mangle. Heavy dirty clothing required special treatment with the heavy, wooden 'dolly'. There was water all over the place, and there was sweat all over Jinsie! In Jinsie's parlance, washing-day was a day for bare sleeves, and many a time did she wipe her forehead on her forearm between trips to the kitchen to see to the dinner. Some wives were reputed to have 'airms like a Clydesdale horse', but Jinsie was of slight build, and the job took toll of her strength.

It was midday before the wash was finished. Then, just as Jinsie was hanging out the last few thingies, her elderly father came on the scene.

'Ye'd better come, Jins! Yer mither's teen anither turn!'

So Jinsie left everything as it was, and went. But first she asked her neighbour Leebie to see that the bairns got their dinner. 'There's a great pot o' tattie soup aa ready, Leebie, an' ye can tak' fit's left t' yersel' an' yer bairns!'

Leebie assured Jinsie that all would be well. 'Jist 'ee gwaa an' see yer mither!'

Jinsie's mither, Kirsten, took 'turns' or 'dwaams' from time to time and, since Jinsie was the nearest to the maternal home, Jinsie was always the first to be called. The reason for the 'turns' was rather obscure, but it was well known that a tayspeenfae o' brandy could work wonders. Jinsie's sister Muggity was uncharitable enough to suggest that it was to get the brandy that her mither took the 'turns'.

'Div ye nae see that she aye needs mair o' the naphtie than she nott the time afore? I'll sweer the aal bizzom's teen a likin' for the stuff! An' her a British Woman anaa!'

Be that as it may, the hard-hearted Muggity was in Yarmouth, so it fell to Jinsie to do the needful, and it was well into the afternoon before Jinsie got hame. There she found that all her washing was out to dry, the dishes had been washed and the fire was burning nicely. But, best of all, there was a fine drappie o' soup left in the pot, enough to make her realise just how hungry she was. Boys, yon wis gran' soup!

'Ye didna tak' ony o' the soup, Leebie?' says Jinsie, later in the afternoon.

'There wisna neen t' tak',' says Leebie. 'Yon quines o' yours fairly kens the wye t' shift their mait! I wis sair made t' get them t' leave a drappie t' yersel'! But, in case ye hinna noticed, I've teen the len' o' yer marra bone, an' we'll hae tattie soup wi't the morn!'

Aye! Times were hard; actually as hard as that! I wis at the school wi' Leebie's loons!

Well, now, Jinsie got her claes in aff the tow jist afore supper time, then it was feeding-time again for the quines. Skirlie was the supper, that nicht, skirlie being oatmeal and sliced ingins fried in very shallow fat. In fact, the best skirlie was toasted/roasted rather than fried, the secret being in the art of not letting the stuff stick to the pan. Jinsie had a chum who was housekeeper to a lawyer in the posh part of town, and this chum would occasionally bring her a bowl of dripping. Only in lawyers' and bankers' houses did ye get dripping . . . fisher folk got fat! Anyhow, skirlie made with the golden dripping was very, very good indeed! Specially when the two really important ingredients were present, namely that the family was always very, very hungry, and skirlie was very, very cheap! Maks a difference, ye ken!

Supper past, Jinsie went back to visit her mither, and advised her father to get Dr Gillespie in the morning if there was no improvement in the 'turns'. The doctor's visit would cost a shillin' or twa, but it was obvious that brandy by itself was merely a stop-gap measure. An' ye didna get brandy for naething, either!

Promising to return at bedtime, Jinsie left her mither's hoose and went home, where she busied herself at shooin' an' darnin'. Her quinies were jist ootside in the streetie, playin' wi' a 'jumpin' rope' an' singin', 'Eevy, ivy, turn the rope over. Mother's at the butcher's buying some beef. Baby's in the cradle, playing with the ladle, one, two, three!'

Jinsie reflected rather sadly that it widna be the morn that Mother wid be at the butcher's buying some beef. It wid hae t' be tatties an' herrin' the morn! Then disaster came, in the form of three distant cousins from another village. They had come for the funeral of an even more distant cousin, an' they could hardly ging hame the morn athoot seein' Jinsie. Jinsie couldna see fit wye they couldna, but she could hardly tell them that! Not that she wasn't pleased to see her folk, but she had naething in the hoose t' gie them! She could hardly offer them loaf an' seerip! Still, the quick-witted Jinsie saw a solution to the problem, so she ran to the door and called her eldest daughter from her skipping.

'Here ye are, my quine! Rin up t' the baker's afore eicht o'clock, an' seek tippenst o' broken biscuit! Hist ye, noo! Hist ye!'

There was method in Jinsie's madness. Tippenst o' vegetables could make a great pot o' broth, tippenst o' lime sufficed to fitewash a washin'-hoose, and tippenst o' broken biscuit, specially near closing time, could come in a great muckle pyoke. An' there micht even be some hale eens amon' them!

Jinsie was back at the door to meet the returning bairn. Oh aye! The bag was big! With the mouth of the bag ticht shut, Jinsie re-entered the living-room where in the presence of her guests, she opened the bag and gazed in assumed horror into its depths.

'Oh dear me! Oh, my govies!' says she. 'Yon craitur's surely faan (fallen) an' broken aa the biscuits!'

Pride an' poverty, Jinsie! Pride an' poverty! But then things were actually as hard as that among the fisher folk! Not in the days of Dickens either, but say 1932/33.

Fizzy Juice

I have a little grand-daughter, three-and-a-half, the apple of mine eye (ye ken the wye o't), who has an inordinate thirst for 'fizzy juice'. The flavour is of secondary importance, as long as the stuff fizzes in her nose! It may well be that you can recall a similar delight from your own childhood, however distant. In those days there were only three flavours … lemonade, cream soda and A.I., the latter title gradually coming to be the comprehensive name for all aerated waters. No doubt you have heard the word 'aiwaan', at least among the fisher folk. Fizzy juice!

It has just occurred to me that I may have coined the term 'fizzy juice', but every time I hear it, I remember Eddie whose surname I have forgotten. Eddie was a Skye man, one of a squad who were laying a pipe from a point near Crossie's, out into the bay. I have never been absolutely sure regarding the primary purpose of the pipe, but I know that its remains can still be seen by anyone walking along Smith's Embankment. At low water, of course! But I do know that, during the laying of the pipe, Eddie sustained a leg injury, and was taken to the Cottage Hospital which, in those days, took all sorts of cases, with the possible exception of heid cases. That itself might not be strictly true, for if being a first class leear means being a heid case, then the place was ram-stam full o' them!

I have it on good authority that a certain schoolboy of that era wrote in an essay ... 'The Cottage is a good place for koffs, koles, an' sair holes an' blisters on your ditty-box!' I have always admired his spelling! I have never doubted his word!

Well, now, a few days after Eddie's admission, I myself arrived on the scene, having been taken ashore from the local M.F.V. Glenugie in the early hours of the morning, under the kindly auspices of Dr Manson, now retired. Suspected 'burst ulcer', or perforation of the stomach lining. Thus did I happen to meet Eddie, and I have never been quite the same since!

As Eddie and I progressed towards recovery, we struck up a friendship of sorts. I really did like the chap, just as I like most West-coasters, the liking being deeply tinged with sympathy, for these people's midgies seem to wear tackety boots! But oh!, the lees! Ye ken iss, boys. I wis fair affrontit at the lees! Some folk think I'm nae a bad han' at it mysel', but I could nivver hud a cannle to Eddie! Maybe it was jealousy that was troubling me. Hour after hour, Eddie shieled them oot, stories which I have stored in my memory for some thirty-seven years. One by one I've weighed them up, and discarded them as being the product of a lively imagination. All save one have met the same fate, but I would like to share with you the one solitary immortal jewel, that it may shine as a light in this sad and ugly world!

According to Eddie, he and his twin brother got a 'holiday jobbie' at a hotel on Skye. For boys in their early teens, there has never been much opportunity on the island, but the hotelier, a distant cousin of their mother's, took the two lads under his wing for a season. Now, the hotel, a mile or two from Portree, wasn't a big one. Say ten or twelve guests at most. But it was quite popular, and it was always completely full throughout the summer months, guests arriving immediately to replace those who had just left. Quite a busy place, and mine host wasn't slow to accept the chance of some cheap labour in the shape of Eddie and his twin, who were employed as odd-job men. No pay, of course, but they would get their grub, and there might be occasional tips from the guests whose shoes they would clean. There would be the two

cows to look after; in fact, there would be a thousand and one jobbies for the loons, all under the orders of the hotel cook.

Now, let's have a look at the cook. She wis a foosty aal fizzer! Forty, at least! She wis a cappernyaam, crabbit aal bizzom. Her nose had been flung on fin her face wis het!. (These terms are mine. It would be pointless to give you Eddie's Gaelic!) To be uncharitable would be unforgivable, so just let's say she made the boys life a misery, and they, in return, vowed to take revenge! But how?

Well, it came to pass in this fashion ... The cook's bedroom on the ground floor of the rear wing had been altered, by means of a thin, floor-to-ceiling partition so that, instead of one quite spacious room, there were now two rather cramped apartments. Cook complained bitterly at the change and vented her spite on the two boys, who slept on a shakkie-doon in the other half. Vision-wise, privacy was perfect. Sound-wise, it was non-existent; the boys could hear every move that Cook made when she retired, about an hour later than they. A slave to habit, as most of us are, she followed the same routine every night.

First, there was the pechs and grunts as she undressed, then came her nightly Gaelic prayer, for she was a devout soul. Her penultimate move, before the creaking bed-springs betrayed her ample weight was to tinkle in her pottie. Same routine, every night. Only by biting hard on the edge of their blanket could the boys prevent themselves from laughing out loud. The coorse craiters! But worse was to come!

On the day, the final day of their employment before going back to school, Eddie's brother thumbed a lift to the nearest chemist's, where he bought three double-size, double-strength, lemon-flavoured Seidlitz powders. Mind you, the flavour wasn't important.

For the enlightenment of the younger generation, let me explain that the Seidlitz powder in a glass of water produces an instant and really ferocious amount of fizz, guaranteed to clear any choked tubes you may have. Gweed help ye if it fizzes in your nose! The boodies 'll flee like caff!

On his return to the hotel, the 'pooder monkey' let his brother see the purchases he had made, and later that evening, while Cook was busy with the dinner, (at eight, you see), the crafty pair crept into her bedroom and scattered the powders into the pottie! To think they could be so coorse!

Bedtime came at last, and the hotel donned its usual nocturnal hush. On the shakkie-doon in the rear bedroom the two rascals lay wide awake in eager expectation, snicherin' now and then as imagination got the better of them. Wasn't Cook later than usual tonight? But the great moment came at last!

If there was anything different that night, it was simply that the tinkle seemed to be somewhat softer than usual. Then, after a split second of deathly silence, a series of agonising and penetrating screams rent the air. Mine host and his startled guests came running, to find Cook in her room, knee-deep in the froth that was yoamin' oot o' the chanty! The only intelligible words in her terrified Gaelic were 'Doctor!', and 'fire in the water!' The rest of her hysterical outburst could probably be summed up in two simple words . . . 'Fizzy juice!'

The loon that conceived the brilliant idea in the first place is now a retired lorry driver. What a loss to the highest Peaks of Learning. With a bittie mair education, he would undoubtedly have made a first-class Fizzicist!

The Greyhound

At a special meeting of the Lustrous Union of Labsters on the 10th of March, 1962, a momentous, unanimous decision was reached, viz . . . 'For the next four months, all labsters will bide in their holes, disregarding the presence of creels, no matter how tempting the bait on view therein'. The meeting was held on the Outers of Scotstown Head, and there was a fairly representative gathering of members of both sexes.

On the same date, at a similar meeting in 25 fathoms off Rattray Head, the Confederation of Carefree Cod passed a resolution that the hale apothick should flit to the Heligoland Bight for an unspecified period. No specific reason was given.

Two days later, off the island of Handa on the west coast, the Union of Migratory Mackerel decreed that, for a six month period, all members were forbidden to round Cape Wrath en route for the North Sea. Disobedience to entail capital punishment.

Now, although Dod and Weelim never actually received typed minutes of these meetings, they kent fine that something was amiss, for poverty was staring them in the face. Times were hard indeed.

'We canna ging on like this!' says Weelim. 'It's nae a case o' keepin' the wolf fae the door, cos he's inower the bed noo! We'll hae t' try something, freen, or we'll be oot o' hoose an' hame.'

'Weel!' says Dod. 'I'm listenin' wi' baith lugs. Can ye come up wi' something, think ye? Jist mine that we're nae so young as we eesed t' be!'

'Fit aboot gettin' a dog?' says Weelim.

'A dog?' says Dod in disbelief. 'A dog? Fit the divvle difference wid a dog mak? Anither mou' t' feed, an' a kirn o' dirt t' redd up. I canna see the sense o' gettin' a dog, for the place is meevin' wi' dogs already.'

'Aha!' says Weelim. 'I dinna mean that kine o' dog ava! I mean a richt dog, a hun dog, a racin' dog!'

'Ye mean a dog for catchin' rubbits! There's a wee bittie o' sense in that, for we could dee wi' a change aff the hairy tatties.'

'I mean a proper greyhound, nae an orra mongrel. Ye mine yon miner that wis here on holiday fae Fife? Weel, he tellt me that he made a heap o' siller aff his dog. Ye see, if ye hiv a fast dog, she wins prize-money, an' ye can aye hae a bet on her forbye, an' that's mair siller! Gweed kens fit we're deein', gaan t' sea for naething!'

'An' far wid ye get sic a dog?' says Dod, showing a little interest.

'Creemin! There's a mannie at Creemin breeds the things, an' he has the fastest dog in Scotlan'. Fin she's gaan full butt, the verra sparks flees oot o' her starn! So he says. Sixty mile an 'oor, nae bother ava!'

'A dog like that wid cost a gey bit,' says Dod. 'Fit's the mannie seekin' for the beastie?'

'I'm nae sure. But she's nae a fire new dog, ye see; she

wid be second han', so we micht get a bittie aff. An' we could go halfs wi the price. Fit div ye say?'

I think it wis the bittie aboot the sparks that made Dod decide, for on the Friday they bocht the dog for seyven powen (cash), but they got ten bob aff for a luck-penny. On the Setterday they took the dog to the races an' put a powen bet on the beast. Boys! She set oot like a rocket, but she feenished hinmaist!

'Deid loss!' says Dod, as they made their way homewards in the evening, wi' a tow roon the dog's neck. 'Fit'll we dee wi' the beast?'

'We could aye shot 'er!' says Weelim.

'Na, na! That wid be cruel!'

'Weel! We could tie a steen roon 'er neck an' droon 'er in the dam, here!'

'Na, na! That wid be cruel!'

'Tell ye fit! We'll jist rin an' leave 'er!'

That was tried, to no avail so, on the Monday they took the dog back to Creemin, only to discover that the mannie had flittit to the Black Isle.

'We're in a richt frap noo!' says Dod. 'Fit can we dee aboot it?'

'I've a cousin at Rathen that's aafa skeely wi' dogs. We could aye ging an' get advice fae him. That winna cost verra muckle, I'm sure!' says Weelim.

The said cousin had a good look at the dog. 'Nae verra muckle wrang, I wid say. Jist a wee bittie hingin'-luggit kine maybe. But ye're still strangers to the craiter, an' she'll maybe buck up a bittie in a day or twa. If I wis you, I wid try giein' her a drappie port wine wi' fite o' egg three times a day. That'll be a great help.'

'Ye may be sure!' says Dod. 'It wid be a great help to mair than the dog!'

Weelim plied the beast faithfully with the mixture, maybe a thochtie ower free wi' the port wine, an' sure as daith, the dog did seem to be mair lively.

It was back to the races on the Saturday, with high hopes of retrieving their losses, the dog apparently rarin' to go. She, of course, had had two doses of her mixture before time for the race an', boys, ye nivver saw the likes o' yon! She gid ben the park like a rippit saithe. 'Seventy mile an 'oor, onywye!' says Dod, though he didna see nae sparks. A hunner yairds aheid o' the field! Great stuff, great rejoicing. All was well!

Prize-money? Hardly! Disqualified cos the dog wis bleezin'. Warned nae to try that again!

Back to the drawing board again, their hairts in their boots. Back to the skeely cousin for a final magic potion.

'Aha!' says he. 'If she can run as fast as that fin she's drunk, she should be able to rin as fast fin she's sober. Try her this wik wi' a bittie fried duff an a drappie sherry, twice a day. Dinna gie her ony on the Saiterday, an' I'll come to the races wi' ye an' watch her rinnin'. There's hope yet!

On the appointed day, the trio took the dog to the field of battle once more. 'Sober as a judge the day.' says Weelim. 'That's nae sayin' muckle!' says Dod.

Before the start of the race, a mannie in a fite coat came and had a look at the dog. 'Ye're aa richt the day, lads! I'm pleased ye've learned yer lesson!'

Well, now, the dog made an excellent start, and was well in the lead at the bend, then she seemed to lose ground and finished in fifth place.

'I see fit's adee wi' the beast!' says the cousin. 'She's aafa fast, but fin she comes to the bend, she swings awa oot to the richt an' the ither dogs is nippin' in atween her an' the pailin'. That's a faat that needs sortin'.'

'Fit wye div ye sort that?' says Dod.

'Oh, it's easy sortit! In fact ye can dee't yersels. Jist get a bittie o' leed, an' fix't on at the back o' her left lug. That'll keep her fae swingin' oot to the richt.'

'A great idea!' says Weelim. 'That shouldna be ill t' dee! Fit's the best wye t' fix't on?'

'Dee't wi' a gun!' was the reply.

Heid First

Maist bairns like a shakkie-doon, specially them that's nivver been on sic a thing! Bairns have aye been like that! It matters little that Dad has the finest car that money can buy ... they want a hurl in a bus. Just let them see something they don't have, (rather difficult nowadays) and Suntie is expected to do the needful, if indeed they can be persuaded to wait that long. Ye ken the wye o't!

Time was when things were rather different! I mean the days when Suntie had somehow run out of toys, and could bring only stockings or boots (never shoes) for boys, and black bloomers or buttoned boots for girls. Of course, he did manage to put a something in the stockings hanging by the mantelpiece ... a puckle shunners (cinders) and an aipple or an orange! What a thrill!

I'm thinking now of two of my pals in the long, long ago, pals who, alas, are no longer with us. They were brithers on a shakkie-doon, and they were on a shakkie-doon because there was nowhere else to put them. As the youngest members of a large family they occupied a very lowly position and, naturally, they longed for promotion. The bed which stood in the same room was not for them, but for an elder brother who was old enough to refuse to sleep three to a bed. Even in the elder brother's absence, the loons were forbidden to occupy the vacant bed which gradually assumed the aura of a holy of holies, a goal to which they ardently aspired. Not that they were not quite comfortable on a shakkie-doon; indeed, it was a very cosy nest, but then, it jist wisna a bed. Ye ken the wye o't!

The elder brother is worthy of further mention, in that he used to sole his younger brothers' boots with the thickest parts of an old tyre, which he used to get from Robertson's garage in York Street. The resultant heavy footwear made the loons fearsome opponents at fitba', in more ways than one. The soles seemed to last forever!

Now, it came to pass that the elder brother upped and offed to some foreign clime, never to return, and thus the loons finally got off the ground, and into the bed. Oh, what bliss to dyste up and doon, tryin' oot the spring! What an experience to gaze down on the basses from the dizzy heights of the old iron bedstead which was itself set up on six inch wooden blocks. This to increase the storage space underneath.

The first night in the bed wasn't a complete success, for they awoke rather earlier than usual. It must be gey early, they thought, for they hadn't yet heard the eight o'clock horn at the Harbour of Refuge, nor could they hear the milk-cairt in the street nor the milkman tellin' the wifies, 'Tsaafa dump 'e day!' In the strange silence they lay for a whilie, surveying the world from an unfamiliar angle. Wasn't the ceiling an 'aafa lot nearer han'?' But the novelty soon wore off, and the pair decided to celebrate their rise in the world by staging a pilla-fecht. Nae rules, jist wallop! Bowff! Thud! Eetya fella! Ooh, ye sod! Ye ken the wye o't!

Well, I suppose it had to come, but Billy got a clour on the side o' the heid that sent him skitin' ower the side, and sink me if he didna land heid-first ... into the dirler! A fine couthie ring aboot that word, isn't there? There was a fine ring aboot it that mornin' for sure, for Billy's great muckle stickin'-oot lugs got jammed ticht into the thing, an' eence his lugs got opened oot, there wis jist nae wye that the dirler wid come aff! So the loon started howlin' pen-and-ink for his mither, whose hasty arrival made matters worse, for she was determined to get the precious utensil off at all costs, it having been a mairridge present, adorned with a bunch of brilliant red roses on its starboard side. But her determined efforts simply inflicted more pain on her protesting offspring, so she had to desist.

There was only one thing she could think of now. Tak' the loon to the doctor! Behold Baabie then, at the front door of yon bonny hoose (now Dodie Donald's shop) where an imposing plate on the gate proclaimed that here resided Dr V. T. B. Yule, who had a veritable alphabet of letters after his name. A first class physician!

'Come in!' says the doctor, rudely aroused. 'Faar's the loon gotten the bonny helmet? Nivver saw the like o't afore!'

So Baabie had to tell him the story, with liberal use of the word 'chanty'. Her pronunciation of the word betrayed

Tired!
Note the footwear.
N. Ritchie, Macduff.

An old cottar house at Coburty, near Rosehearty.

An old-style ploughing match near Turriff. (1988)
Courtesy *Aberdeen Journals*.

The Boddam bus in the author's childhood. Note the 'half-crown bonnets' usually paid at sixpence per week.

her alien origins, for had she been a native of the Blue Toon, the 'a' would have been a 'u'.

'Well, Mrs Buchan, I'm afraid there's got to be a sacrifice here the day! It's the loon or the po! Ye canna hae them baith!'

Wi' the greet in her throat, Baabie agreed that the helmet was expendable, so the doctor got a candyhaimmer fae the kitchen to shatter the thing. Then Baabie grat richt! Jist a proper greetin' match, wi' the loon howlin' anaa!

'Fit'll ye be needin' for this, noo, Doctor?' says Baabie, for in those days the doctor had to be paid.

'Naething this time, Mrs Buchan. I'll pit this doon to experience, but stand by if there's a next time!'

Once back at home, Baabie fell oot on the son who had dealt the fearful blow in the first place. He, poor soul, bolted for school as soon as he had swallowed his porridge, leaving his brother to have his assorted scarts and bruises bathed. Then there was another tooin' match, for Billy suddenly realised he was late for school, and would need a 'notie for the teacher'. Now, even though there had been any note-paper in the house, it's more than likely that Baabie would have declined to use it, for she was by no means the world's best writer. So Billy was sent packing, to make his own excuses. It is a pity indeed that Miss Strachan's reaction when she was confronted with 'Please, Miss, I fell into the po!', has not been recorded.

Later that day, Baabie went 'up the toon' to seek a replacement for the broken pot, and eventually found one to her liking in Grant & Black's in Marischal St. Plain china this time; no rose motif! She failed to grasp the meaning of the assistant's words when he advised her that the proper title for the receptacle was 'a goes-under'. She also firmly declined to have the object 'rowed up'.

'There's nae need for a boddy to be affrontit at that, surely!'

Behold Baabie now, her left hand clutching her pursie and her shawl at the same time, and the great muckle pot dangling from her right wrist. She was completely heedless of the amused glances of the passers-by, as she made her way along Chapel Street towards the fish shop. Her 'hairt wis warsh for a bittie fish!'

The fishmonger in Queen Street was Jim Lewis, a newcomer, and a Welshman to boot. Not a word of the Doric did he understand, so Baabie would have to 'talk' to him. How she hated to use English! But it had to be done!

Once inside the shop, Baabie hitched the great, enormous pot onto the counter, to free her right hand for ficherin' in her pursie.

'Pound a fillit!' says she, talking posh.

'A fiver you don't!' says Jim.

Peer Baabie!

Jockie

Jockie is one of the few remaining survivors of the race once known as the 'fisher folk'. Although he is, by some fifteen years, my senior, he has been a friend of mine for as long as I can remember – and even longer than that, if such a thing is possible. And, when I use the word 'friend', I would, in Jockie's case give it a capital 'F' for, according to Proverbs, a friend loveth at all times! So there you have Jockie, my lifelong mentor and occasional critic.

Born into a fisher household, Jockie was suckled on the Scriptures and steepit in the Psalms, Kirk to the backbone. Even today he will unerringly name any Psalm tune he hears. Give him the first line of the words, and he'll tell you the number of the Psalm and the tune required. Not for him the 23rd Psalm to the tune 'Crimond'! 'Orlington', or 'Covenanters', certainly! But 'Crimond!' Nivver! Fashious, think ye? Well, a wee bittie, maybe, but in things pertaining to the Kirk, Jockie has aye been fashious! As long as he was able, Jockie attended morning worship in the Kirk, the only exception being those Sundays which found him in some Hielan' loch, where the service in the local Kirkie was sure to be in Gaelic. One of the Old Brigade, to be sure.

As soon as he went to school, Jockie had to learn English, from scratch. Oh, he had a few Sunday School texts which he could recite, parrot fashion, but such material, thickly overlaid with a strong North-east accent, was no substitute for the real thing. So it was actually to a foreign language that Jockie and his contemporaries had to address themselves. Their vast vocabulary of local words and phrases, in which they were so amazingly articulate, was of no use whatsoever in an English-speaking world. And, as is usually the case in any foreign-language class, some of the youngsters were outstanding. Most of them managed to scrape through, but a few never really got off the ground, finding great difficulty in mentally translating their own speech into a foreign tongue while actually speaking. For these boys, English has always been and always will be their second language! If circumstances dictate that English be used, highly intelligent and fluent speakers are suddenly ill at ease in a medium not naturally theirs. In fact, they seem to be 'feart' at it, and in their hesitancy, they make some wonderful mistakes.

Jockie went to sea at a very early age, jist a loon in his Deydie's ripper boatie, but his eye was always on bigger boats and farther horizons. He ended his fishing career in a ripper yole with two of his grandsons as crew. 'Jist bairns!', he called them, but now these same bairns are on the Bergen and Viking Banks in the depth of winter, and even as far as Rockall in boats which are not really big enough for such waters. Such is life!

Nowadays, Jockie comes but seldom to the harbour, although he rarely misses the Kirk, where he laments the disappearance of the Psalms and Paraphrases. 'Things is nae the same, noo!' is an expression very often on his lips as he sits at home, reminiscing on days gone by, in his aul-farrant tongue, so broad that his younger grandchildren fail to understand the half of what he says. He likes to speak of the old times, the long, lean years of famine which his generation had to endure. And one winter in particular, when the local baker, in his horse-drawn van, made a nightly round of the village to distribute FREE loaves among the starving fishers. 'Fin EE get it, then I'LL get it!' seemed to be the motto of the local shopkeepers who supplied the fisher populace with all manner of goods, on tick! There was no dole, and no D.H.S.S. Can you wonder that the old fella says 'Things is nae the same, noo!'

Those were the days when, if the season had been reasonably good, Jockie would pay the tailor for the beautiful hairback (heavy serge) breeks he had got the year before, then he would order a new suit of navy blue serge, on the same understanding ... 'Fin EE get it, then I'LL get it!' Every fisherman had his hairback breeks, always tailor-made, and always with front pockets. The colour would vary from village to village, from dark brown to black. Mine were black. The hairback breeks and the home-knitted jersey were the fisherman's 'go-ashores', kept neatly folded in his suitcase on the shelf in his bunk.

Now, there are those who will assume that Jockie, with his steadfast love for the Kirk and his deep interest in things spiritual, must be a 'doom and gloom' sort of chap, preaching Hell fire and eternal damnation. Not so, Jockie, for he is really good company with his dry wit and his keen sense of humour. He is very fond of the true story of an old widowed fisherman whom we both knew in our youth.

Apparently, this fella advertised for a housekeeper and, when the first suitable applicant appeared, he proceeded to show her the house.

'Noo!' says he. 'Iss is 'e kitchen, an' 'at's 'e front room. An' up 'e stairs here – 'iss is oor bedroom!'

'Hey!' says she. 'Fit div ye mean, OOR bedroom?'

'Weel!' says he, 'It widna be richt o' me t' hae my neepers tellin' lees aboot me!'

And Jockie can tell a story against himself, forbye. Came the day the minister asked him to give a vote of thanks at the annual Kirk 'siree'. Only prood an' bigsy folk used the work 'swaree'. For fisher folk it wis aye 'siree'. I once heard a shipmate describe the Mission mannie's fite bonnet as being like 'a siree table!' Nae bad!

'Now, John!' says the minister. 'You are our oldest member, and I'd be delighted if you would bring the evening to a close by giving the vote of thanks!'

'Na, na, minister! Nae me! I wid be sure t' miss somebody oot! An' that wid be blue murder! Ye ken that.'

'No problem, John! I'll give you a copy of the complete programme, so you cannot possibly miss anybody! What about it?'

'Na, minister! I canna hannle the gran' English words.

I'm sure t' say something vrang, an' mak' a feel o' masel'. Specially wi' aa yon folk listenin'!'

'If you stick closely to your script, John, you cannot possibly go wrong! And as for your grammar and pronunciation, I'm sure nobody will be looking for flawless English! In fact, such a thing would be completely out of character. As long as the audience knows exactly what you mean, all will be well. C'mon, John, say you'll do it!'

Very, very reluctantly Jockie agreed to do the needful, and the siree duly took place. A richt fine nicht, a gran' nicht! Everybody got a baggie o' cookies as they entered, tea to be at half time; milk or A.I. (lemonade) for the bairns for fear they micht be brunt wi' the het tay. At the close of the evening's entertainment, ilkie bairn would be given an orange, the only orange they would see until the next siree!

The programme was lengthy and varied, most of the congregation taking part in some way or another. The singing was of a very high standard, for the fisher folk of those days loved to sing their spiritual songs in four part harmony. Indeed, they really excelled in the art! There was the occasional slight discord when some restless loon would fire a pandrop at his chum on the other side of the hall, but otherwise the event was quite peaceful.

Jockie sat there enjoying himself, for he simply loved singing. Then, at the close, he was called upon to round things off in the usual way. This he did in splendid fashion, considering that this was his first attempt at public speaking. Not a soul did he forget to mention, and he resumed his seat to great applause, feeling rather proud of his performance.

Then, as mithers rowed graavits roon their bubbly-nibbit bairns before facing the bitter cold outside, and as fathers swopped opinions as to which item had been the best, disaster overtook Jockie, for he sprang to his feet to announce in a most apologetic tone,

'Ladies an' gintlemin, I'm aafa sorry, but I forgot t' thunk Mrs Duthie for the len' o' her urine (urn) for makkin' the tay!'

I tellt ye English wis a foreign language!

Piz Meal

I have read more than once that, out of doors, it is never really dark. This has often made me wonder just how dark a night has to be to qualify for the title 'Really Dark'. There are degrees of darkness, just as there are degrees of light but by which yardstick does one measure darkness?

It is really amazing how readily the human race can adapt itself to the dark, as the war-time blackouts proved. Mind you, in those days, most of the populace were in familiar surroundings, and found no great difficulty in getting around, although there were several sad fatalities, even among natives. I would say that, if a boddy has any problem negotiating his own neighbourhood, then it's 'Really Dark'.

I remember quite clearly a night in 1942, when I was on the way from the Roanheads to Jamaica Street via the Hillock and the Longate. I bumped into a pedestrian of some kind, and there followed the usual apologies, but I'm not sure yet whether it was a little mannie wi' a beard or a great muckle chiel wi' a kilt. I'm tellin' ye, it wis gey dark!

Speaking of darkness, let me tell you about Jeems and Leebie, an elderly couple who lived in one of the coastal villages of Buchan in the not-so-long-ago. Their hoosie was simply a butt-an'-ben, two rooms with a closetie between. There was no back door to the house, neither was there a supply of running water, a sad, but common fact which decreed that, within the house, there could be no sanitation. Primitive? Maybe, but most houses in Buchan were exactly the same. One simply made one's own arrangements, especially when the little wooden shack at the rear of the house was occupied.

In spite of these drawbacks to their humble abode,

Jeems and Leebie had reared a family of three sons and two daughters, all of them now up and away to homes and families of their own. So the old couple were left alone in the cottage where they had begun their wedded life, but now, according to Leebie, 'the dookit wis far ower big for twa doos!' When in reminiscent mood, they would remember the hurley-bed, a great muckle box on castors, a bed which could be 'hurled' in aneth the box bed during the day, to be hurled out again in the evening when it was bairns' bed time. In those times, space had been at a premium, but now it was all so different.

The couple now lived, ate and slept in the one room, which was never known as anything but the 'kitchen'. The single coal fire supplied all their heating requirements, the room being very snug indeed, especially when the Tilley lamp, a great source of heat in itself was lighted. But there had been a drastic change in the couple's nocturnal habits. You see, when the bairns had been on the go, Leebie had claimed the front berth in the box-bed, so that she could readily attend to her brood during the night. Jeems was banished to the back, hard against the wall, and many a time was he exhorted to 'Lie doon an' be quaet!'

Now their lifestyle was different in that Jeems was at the front, simply to facilitate his frequent nocturnal answers to the call of Nature. As Leebie put it, 'Ye're forivver rinkin' aboot throwe the nicht, so ye'd better tak' the front an' gie a boddy a meenit's peace!'

Jeems, unfortunately, was a martyr to what I have heard described as 'the aal man's trouble'. In modern parlance, that simply means problems with the prostate gland, but in Jeems's day very few among the working class had ever heard of such a thing. The complaint was very common indeed, and it would seem that there was little that the medical men of the period could do about it.

I remember very clearly how the all-male members of the Parliament which used to meet at the Cannon seemed to take it in turns to ging doon the steps a bittie to relieve themselves. Many a time have I, as a barfit loon, made my way up and down these steps on the outside of the railing, to avoid the stinking mess. The steps at the foot of Merchant Street were even worse, cos they could be smelt as far away as the Toonshoose. Oh gyaad!

But, let's get back to the story, instead of revelling in gory details of the good old days.

It was very close to Christmas, according to the calendar, but not according to anything else, for Christmas was simply another date. It was a time of going to work, it was a time for going to sea. Oh, aye! The bairns would sing their carols in day-school and in Sunday School, and Christmas hymns were the order of the day in the Kirks on Christmas Sunday, but Christmas Day itself was never a holiday. Not in this neck of the woods. You see, Suntie came on Hogmanay, and New Year's Day was the holiday (one day only).

'What a pagan practice!' you may say. Well, maybe . . . maybe. But thousands of devout souls would have it no other way.

Christmas, (not the Message of Christmas, which we had known and loved all our days) Christmas came to these parts with the oil, and the gas, and the Yanks, and the English, and all the other foreigners. That's how recent it is. Now we have at least a fortnight of gluttony and drunkenness, and a period of profligate spending which, at times, borders on the obscene. If it is not pagan, it certainly isn't Christian. Having sampled both ways, I'm for the old way, every time.

Well, now, it was getting very close to Christmas, and Jeems was in his appointed place at the front of the bed. The strong northerly wind kept up a miserable whining noise at the window, a whine that increased to a roar in the lum when a wintry shower spattered on the roof. Although the fire had gone out, the room was still snugly warm, and Jeems was, to say the least, very cosy. Then came the strong, clear call that could not be denied! 'The door, Jeems! At your hardest!' I might be better to point out that it wasn't the call of the sea. So Jeems obeyed instantly . . . he could do no other. Could he but make the door, he would get it open and relieve himself into the night.

He was in the very act when Leebie cried . . . 'Watch that Suntie disna see ye! But it's nae likely he'll be aboot on a nicht like this!'

'It's a richt fine nicht here!' says Jeems. 'There's nae a breath o' win' noo, an' there's a richt fine smell o' piz meal!'

'Come oot o' there, ye orra breet!' was the reply. 'Come oot o' that! Ye're into the press!'

Faa said it was 'never really dark?'

Wull's Chariot

In the distant days of my boyhood there were certain times when I was very well off. These were the red-letter days when I could afford to go to the Picters either in Aubrey's, opposite the end of Chapel Street, or in Clarkie's, in Hanover Street. Mind you, the Saturday afternoon matinee cost tippence, so I wasn't there very often, coppers being rather hard to come by. But I recall quite vividly the thrill of sitting in the front seats, gazing up at the flickering screen until there was a crick in my neck. Those were the days of the silent films, but the hubbub among the junior audience could be quite something. You see, all the dialogue appeared on the screen in print, and there was always a certain element who, apparently, could only read aloud. Most annoying! Still, I was rather jealous of a classmate of mine who got to the picters at least once a week, simply to read the titles to an old man who couldn't read at all. It's an ill wind . . .

Love scenes were anathema to me, but I fairly likit cowboys and Indians, pirates and gladiators, and above all, Ben Hur. What a scare you could get when the chariots seemed to be about to leave the screen and come right into the front stalls. Same with films about express trains; there had to be shots where the train was coming straight at you. Good grief, yon fairly scared the flechs aff ye! By the way, it simply isn't true that every patron of Clarkie's was supposed to get a candy-hammer along wi' their ticket, to slay the flechs. That applied only to a certain place in Aiberdeen, and that was hine, hine awa!

After seeing Ben Hur, there was a lengthy period when we all pranced along the pavements like a puckle horses, stopping now and then to nicher like feels and to paw the ground like Arab stallions, (not advisable with bare feet among chuckie steens). I'm jist thinkin' that, had there been wheelie bins on the go at that time, they would have been commandeered as chariots. There would have been no shortage of horses. Practically every fisher loon wanted a chariot as a Yarmouth present, but the chariots didn't materialise. Next year, maybe.

Not until I was several years older did I learn that there was actually a chariot in the toon, and a vary famous chariot at that! And, what was more, it was a fisher chariot, with a constant supply of human horses, available at somewhat peculiar hours. Jist wyte a meenit, an' I'll tell ye aa aboot it.

In the days when the railway came right down to the Harbour. There was a large goods yard which became the site of today's patent slipway. From there the rails ran close behind the old Coastguard Station (on their right) then close along the rear of the curing yards in Wilson Road (on their left), with Ives Park on their right, under the Brig in Ugie Street, close to that hideous brick building which was once the Electricity Station for the town; thence through Raemoss Park to the Station Yard.

At the foot of Port Henry Road there was an imposing footbridge for the benefit of pedestrians wishing to reach the seaward part of the Roanheads, known as 'Ower the Wickets'. There were, apparently, at one time wicket gates in the railway fencing to permit the public to cross the rails. Whether or not these gates gave rise to the name 'Wickets', they had disappeared long before my time, although the name remains.

Now, to find our chariot, we maun ging ower the Wickets. I have called it 'Wull's Chariot', but it was never actually Wull's at all, since it belonged to Alex Summers, Fishmerchant (Killer's father). And it was never a proper chariot, but simply a great long hurley with rubber-shod cab wheels, quite easy to hurl if you had it properly balanced. The primary purpose of the hurley was to transport boxes of fish, although it could be utilised for other purposes as the occasion arose.

So, why Wull's Chariot? Faa wis Wull? Wull (Taylor) bedd ower the Wickets in what is now a richt bonny hoosie of dressed granite with a little porch in front. I never kent Wull, but I did ken his sons Jock an' Towdie, known world wide as the 'Wells o' Wearie'. On the occasions when my Deydie sent me to see Wull's Boys aboot gettin' the len' o' their boatie to shoot a bit sma'line in Shumfirt (Sandford Bay), I met the other son Wucksie, who was at that time a bedall (chronic invalid).

'Faa did ye say yer Deydie wis?'

'Aal Oxy's my Deydie!'

'Aa richt, loon, tak' the yole awa!'

Fine, quaet, hairmless men they were; Pilots in the days when Pilotage was a cut-throat business. There were several Pilots, each with his own boat, the rule being that first aboard the ship was the accepted Pilot. Competition, did ye say? Bleed an' hair's mair like it! The 'Wells', having only a rowing boat, stood little chance against the others with their motor engines. It was all a matter of speed, you see.

But there was one remarkable occasion when the tortoise outran the hare, so to speak.

A big steamer had landed half her cargo of salt in Wick, and was on the way to Peterhead with the other half. It was common knowledge that she was coming, so the Pilots watched each other like hawks, lest one should steal a march on the others. Finally, one decided to go north to meet the ship, but he was scarcely clear of the piers before another three boats were on his tail. The poor 'Wells' simply couldn't compete, so they just sat tight. Now, it came to pass that, in dense fog, the four motor boats missed the ship completely, and this proved to be a proper windfall for the Wells, for the steamer arrived off Peterhead and lay hooting for a Pilot, just a few hundred yards from the Wells' door. Of course they seized the opportunity, and piloted the ship into port. What a prize.

The sad part of the story is that, when the motor boats returned after a long, fruitless chase, one of the skippers was so incensed on seeing the ship snugly berthed that he went to Almanythie Creek and put a great muckle steen through the bottom of the poor men's boatie. Such a noble thing to do, wasn't it?

The mention of speed reminds me of the time when Nep (meaning 'hairy'), one of the local pilots bought a second-hand pinnace from the Navy. She was long and thin, like a sunnel (sand eel), with a 60 hp Kelvin, and she was very fast indeed. But she proved to be 'ower sair on the paraffin', and never really was a success. Of course the arrival of this peculiar craft was a nine days wonder. Even Dr Taylor was told about Nep's new pinnace but, since the good doctor's informant mispronounced the word, as

most of the old fishermen did, you can well imagine the consternation among the medical fraternity. Transplants 60 years go? Nivver!

Boys, we're awa fae the chariot aathegither! I suppose it's my blame, so I'll tell ye aboot the chariot noo.

Wull was a fisherman with a wife and three sons. The wifie kept a spotless hoosie, and saw to it that her menfolk were aye 'weel in order'. Sadly, when the Mither died, the men-folk lost the place as men-folk are so prone to do when bereft. The guiding hand was gone, and the Demon Drink took command, until the tow gid wi' the bucket. Enter, now, the Chariot.

It was a long-standing arrangement that, at closing time on Saturday night (nine o'clock) the hurley should be at the door of Mother Aiken's pub (now the Christian Bookshop). On the stroke of nine, the four warriedrags emerged, laden with their previously purchased groceries and singing melodiously 'The bonnie Wells o' Wearie', a song they were particularly fond of. As soon as the passengers had draped themselves on the Chariot, the horses took off at a fearsome rate. There was never a shortage of loons to act as horses. Doon the brae as hard as they could go; it's a miracle they didna land in Port Henry, makkin' for the Wickets. The noisy procession must needs pass Ailick Summers' hoose, where a very articulate parrot enjoyed the sea air in a cage which hung from a nail in the gable. On hearing the rabble, the parrot screamed, 'Drucken Wull, Drucken Wull!' sending Wull, on the Chariot, almost berserk, thinking that it was bairns jeering at him. But worse was to come.

There was a gate in the low dykie in front of Wull's hoosie, too narrow for the Chariot to enter. Fine did the loons ken that, so, on the last lap they gathered speed along the middle of the road before swinging the Chariot towards the gate. Of course the Chariot stopped with a thud, but the passengers gid skitin' on, to land in a discordant heap at the very door. Strangely, they never seemed to be any the worse. The loons, of course, thought it was great fun.

Only once did I witness this amazing performance, and I never went back.

I dinna like to greet!

A Prile of Kings

For as long as I can remember, I have been on speaking terms with Royalty. Not the British Monarchy, of course, but a line of Kings, all the same. Such a claim might give you the idea that I am one of the Royal Buchans, but that would be entirely false, for I am not a Royal Buchan at all. In fact, I'm not even a Pirate Buchan, but purely and simply a common five-eight Tinkie Buchan.

How did I find that out? Long and patient research, boys, and a sixth sense.

It transpires that I am a direct descendant of the first traceable Tinkie Buchan who lost his life at Culloden. That's richt, boys, he wis killt! Not that he was actually at the battle, but he had a tintie in the neist park, an' gid ower to compleen aboot the din! R.I.P.

Be that as it may, and I see no reason to doubt it, I have known several Kings in my time, but sad to say, they're getting rather thin on the ground now, and the world is all the poorer for their passing.

The first King I met was the Pearl King, Mr Birnie of Wellbank, who made a fortune out East somewhere at the pearling game. I suppose that nowadays he would be called an entrepreneur, but in those days that word was unknown. He's the man who provided the money for the building of the Birnie Brig. £2,500 it was then, but I doubt if you could get it whitewashed for that money now. I was at the opening ceremony in 1925, and got a chocolate egg, as did all the other bairns in the town. My egg lasted some forty seconds, but I ken that some youngsters kept their eggs as a souvenir, till the chocolate was foosty. Silly asses!

Now, how did I come to ken the Pearl King? Well, ye see, my Deydie scuttered aboot wi' smaalins (haddock lines), and it was universally considered that nothing but horse hair was suitable for making the 'tippins', to which the hooks were attached. Since there were several hundred hooks on a line, quite a lot of horse-hair was required. Now, I suppose the milkman, or any of the numerous carriers could have supplied the hair, but Deydie believed in going to the fountainhead, and that was up the country. He also believed that I was somehow a necessary companion on his meanderings around the rural scene, in search of horse-hair for his linies or 'speyngie' (osiers) for his basket-weaving. A versatile kind o' mannie, apparently.

Thus did I, at a very tender age, and on foot, become acquaint wi' country folk in cottage and in mansion, at the same time discovering that the ripper codlin' is a strong, hard, reliable currency. You know, that is one thing that has never changed throughout the years.

So that's how I came to meet, on several occasions, Alexander Birnie Esq. of Wellbank, the Pearl King.

The second King in my prile was the King of Denmark. Not that I ever got the length of Denmark, for the said King was a Peterhead man, whose domicile was somewhere in yon close which takes you from the Broadgate to the North Shore (or vice versa). I have no idea how he got his bye-name, although I have tried to find out, but his real name was Keith Forbes, and I think a boddy wid be sair made to find a mair 'Peterheid' name than that! Somehow my mind associates such a name with 'Veritas Vincit'.

The King of Denmark was a rather roch sort of character who, in his cups on Saturday night, would come onto the Broadgate wearing his nicky-tams, and with his sark open to the waist, ready to challenge the world. Sad to say, the challenge was sometimes accepted by one of the many hardy sons of Lewis who were so much a part of the local scene at that time, and there were some richt stashies, I can tell ye. Bleed an' hair, an' bad words! Far better than the picters. Eetya, fella! That's where I got my extensive vocabulary of swear words, both Doric and Gaelic. Of course, I never use them, but I keep them in a boxie, handy kind, ye see! Maybe some day I'll get a glossary, so's I'll ken fit I'm sayin'.

Keith was one of the many 'coal heavers' in the town, the hardy men who walked the bending, swaying planks with ten-stone bags of coal on their backs, to replenish the drifters' bunkers. Hard, dangerous work. These men also unloaded the cargoes of coal from the Northumbrian ports, shovelling the coal into great muckle iron buckets.

(No grabs in those days.) Same with the great cargoes of dazzling white salt from the Mediterranean, or from Spain. Sheer hard labour. And let's not forget the timmer trade with the Baltic ports and the long-forgotten republics of Estonia, Latvia and Lithuania. Good for your geography!

Came the Thirties, and the great Depression. Coopers by the score were laid off, and spent their time taking long walks round by Inverugie. Did you know that, at one time, on the Queenie alone there 90 coopers making barrels? The coal-heaver/stevedore community felt the severe draught at the same time, and it was most distressing to see so many decent, hardworking men on the scrap heap.

In those days I was a beginner as a fisherman in a 40ft. boatie, landing flukes every night, sair made to get a living. Prominent among my many memories of that time are the occasions when we would put a herring basket of dabs on the quay for the benefit of the unemployed, most of whom seemed to have a bittie o' wire in their pooch. Jist the verrra dunt for stringin' on a fry! Most of them said 'Thank-you!' but when the King of Denmark said 'God bless ye, my loon!' I somehow felt that it was sincere. You have simply no idea how quickly the dabs in that basket disappeared. Mind you, there was a whilie when we were not very popular with the 'chippers' in the town. Well, what were they but unscrupulous profiteers, charging fourpence for a fish supper?

The third member of my prile of Kings was the Podley King, Wallim's Sandy. Aabody kent Sandy, and especially the bairns, who listened entranced to his tales. A quiet, hairmless soul was Sandy, wi' a something aboot 'im that ye couldna pit yer finger on. It would appear that, as a boy he was perfectly normal, until he was bitten by a dog. Thereafter he was never the same. But he haunted the piers, summer and winter, part of the fittings, the Podley King. Oh, I ken there were other claimants to the title, but they were only Pretenders; the Crown was Sandy's, without a doubt!

Behold Sandy then, at the end of Port Henry pier, where the north entrance used to be. Just watch in amazement as his catch of podleys accumulates at his back, where he has thrown them one by one, without looking round; and be prepared to gasp in horror as the great heap

of fish slides forward and pushes Sandy into the sea! Never was there a fisherman to equal him. Well do I remember a photograph in one of the glossy magazines ... 'The fisher, after a week of unremitting toil, wends his way home'. It was Sandy on the Model Jetty with a fry of herring, scranned from the old drifter Boy Willie. Well, why not? He had been out of the house for at least an hour and a half!

Then there was the remarkable occasion when Sandy, given a pound to go for messages, inadvertently allowed it to fall into the fire, where it was instantly consumed. Now, although the pound was all the money in the house, all was not lost, for there were eight glittering half-crowns in the ash-pit in the morning! Such good fortune happens only to Kings.

I shall never forget the story Sandy told me, concerning his own days at sea. Apparently Sandy was deck-hand on a coaster bound from Blyth to Peterhead with a cargo of Shilbottle coal. When the ship was passing Collieston, about two miles off, it was observed that a tremendous number of birds were diving and picking at something in the ship's wake. Nobody paid much attention. Then Sandy, on instructions from the Skipper to draw a bucket of water 'for to wash down the decks', discovered in the bucket of water seven live herrings. So the birds had actually been feasting on herring thrown up by the ship's propeller! Boys! They must have been thick!

On arriving at Peterhead, Sandy found his fishermen friends in dark despair, for the herring shoals had forsaken their normal haunts, and famine was staring everybody in the face. Nevertheless, on Sandy's instructions, they all with one accord launched out into the deep for one final go. The result was better than even Sandy had expected. Next morning, special trains brought women from the Broch to handle the miraculous catches, and for seven weeks thereafter the fishers prospered exceedingly. A wonderful story, all the more so for the fact that Sandy was never afloat in his life!

Sandy, with his wrist bones like foremast shackles and his hands like shovels. Sandy, with the faraway look in his clear blue eyes. Sandy in his Sunday attire of collarless shirt, with a woollen scarf crossed loosely on his chest beneath a well worn jacket. Sandy, a faithful Salvationist, yet no respecter of denominational boundaries, worshipping with every sect in turn, as the Spirit led. Sandy, the Podley King, but a King also in the fact that he knew no discontent.

Have we any Kings about the place today? We have quite a few Barons (to use the fisher term for successful skippers); we may have more than one millionaire. But both these types will be forgotten as soon as they are buried.

There is, however, about Kings, a peculiar lasting quality. Where, oh where has that gone?

Fire and Film-Stars

The Great Fire of London must have been a fair bleeze! A hale toon on fire at the same time! Apparently it was a blessing in disguise, for it put an end to the great plague (The Black Death) which had been raging in the city for so long. I have wondered, more than once, if the Great Fire was started deliberately.

According to Peter Buchan, no relation of mine, there was a fire among the huts which had been erected on the braes, just to the north of the Blue Toon, as a sort of isolation hospital for victims of the same plague, and wasn't there some suspicion of fire-raising then too?

Both of these fires have been well recorded, but the Great Fire of Peterhead has been allowed to fade into oblivion. What a shame! You see, it happened like this …

In the days before road-laying machines were invented, our streets were tarred in the old-fashioned way which required the presence of a tar boiler. The boiler was simply a huge iron tank set on iron wheels, a tank with a furnace beneath it, and a great lang lum stickin' up at the front. Not a beautiful sight! The tar (from the gas-works, I believe), was brought to the boil before being drawn off via great muckle brass cocks into 'roosers', to be carried by roadmen and sprayed on the ground. Then other members of the gang scattered chuckie steenies on the hot tar. A very labour-intensive process, a hot, dirty, smelly job!

There was one very good aspect to the smell, in that it was reputed to be beneficial to bairns wi' the 'kink-hoast' (whooping cough), that terrifying ailment, now completely eradicated by modern medicine. Doctors did actually advise mothers to take their suffering infants 'round past the gas-works, or close to the tar boiler!' The tar boiler was towed, of course, to wherever it was required.

Now, then, one day, in Marischal Street, the boiler 'devulped' (I quote) a hole in its boddim, allowing the boiling tar to run down through the furnace to the gutter below. The great, black clouds of smoke blotted out the sun, and the street was like a dark tunnel with a river of fire running through it. What a sicht! To see a park o' barley strae burnin' on a dark nicht, would give you some idea of what it was like. Most of the shop-fronts in the street suffered paint damage, but the most serious casualty was Mackintosh, the baker's, (Walter Allan's). There the windows were utterly destroyed, and the blind burnt to a cinder. The Post Office, too, suffered badly.

Now, it simply isn't true that Johnny Millar abandoned ship, nor is it true that Mackintosh put a boxie on the coonter boldly marked 'For the Blind'. Fa wid say sic a thing? But it is a fact that several 'tows o' claes' were destroyed by soot. Some would have it that the fall-out from the tarry cloud exterminated the kink-hoast throughout the whole of Buchan! But let me tell you now of something which really happened.

The week after the fire, some visiting Dutch fishermen stopped to survey the damage to Mackintosh's shop. Then one of them, probably the cook, entered the shop and asked for 'meelick'.

'Oh, aye!' says the chiel at the coonter. 'We've plinty o' that! Jist hold on!' He was back from the bake-hoose in a meenit, wi' a great muckle pyoke o' mealicks (crumbs).

The Dutchman shook his head vigorously. 'Meelick! Meelick! Meelick!'

It was only after the visitor had sat on a biscuit tin, miming the milking of a cow, and roarin' like a spent calf, that it was realised that he wanted milk. Then he was sent elsewhere. See how great a barrier language can be?

This reminds me of an incident during the war years when, for a while, I was engineer on a former Lossie fishing boat, the Tulip. A crew of Norwegians, ex-fishers, arrived to take up duty on an ex-Clyde ringer with a 44 hp Kelvin Diesel. Now, the Kelvin Diesel, and especially the 44, has a rather alarming knock when running slow, although the knock disappears at higher revs. In some alarm the Norwegian reported to the Base Engineer Officer who, being a steam man, knew nothing about diesels.

'Go and see Peter on the Tulip!' says he. 'Peter knows all about diesels!'

That, of course, wasn't strictly true, but it resulted in our having a stranger with us at tea-time, a stranger who had very little English, and no experience at all in Scottish built engines. He was extremely worried about the 'very heavy knocking' (you must pronounce the first K) in his engine. I managed to tell him, mostly by sign language, that he should have supper with us, then I would have a lookie at the Kelvin. He seemed to enjoy his spam and powdered egg, conversing with me all the time as best he could.

Having spent an hour with my new friend, allaying his fears and teaching him a few things about his tattered instruction book, I returned to my ship, to be greeted with warm admiration from the skipper.

'Man, Peter!' says he. 'Ye're a great lad! Ye can fairly spik t' the foreigners! I hardly kent a word the chiel said!'

'Och!' says I, with commendable modesty. 'Languages disna gie me ony bother ava! Jist nae neen!'

'I see that! But tell me this! Fit wye dis yon chiel ken Humphrey Bogart? He wis aye spikkin' aboot 'im!'

This had me puzzled for a meenit. Then the answer came to me.

'He wisna spikkin' aboot Humphrey Bogart ava! He wis jist thinkin', fin he haard the 'very heavy knocking (pronounce the first K) that his engine was bogart!'

See what the language barrier can do?

Bad Words Ashore and Afloat

I have seen some folk wince visibly at the sound of certain words which are normally described as 'four-letter words'. For a start, that is a misnomer, for many of the really bad words comprise six or more letters. Not that it makes any difference to me, for I can get along quite nicely without them. Oh, I know that some fellas seem utterly incapable of speech without the liberal use of offensive terms, but that is simply a bad habit, of which they are apparently unaware. Others again, under intense pressure, let themselves go completely, to suddenly become very articulate men indeed instead of the quiet, reserved chaps they had been, only a minute earlier. There are those who, in the face of such outbursts turn their faces away as if physically struck, there are others who lift their eyes skyward while their lips offer silent orisons. Sad to say, from experience, I have found such folk to be, as a rule, not completely sincere. And then there's me. In such circumstances I am possessed with an insane desire to laugh, and I canna help it! I lach, an' lach till I'm gey near greetin'. I must be feel aathegither, surely!

Picture, now, if you can, a bonny, warm, sunny mornin' on the broad fields o' Buchan, and behold me bizzin' along the road like yon kind o' bee that I've tellt ye aboot afore, and jist watch as a fairmer, apparently in some distress flags me doon.

'Foo many pints is there in the compass, Peter?' An' him a fairmer!

'I'll rattle them aff, an' ye can coont them yersel',' says I.

'Hinna time for that! Nae time!' says he. 'But somebody'll hae t' pint me in some direction, afore I ging feel!'

'Fit's adee?' says I, sensing that the peer breet wis at high doh. 'Hiv ye lost yer wuts?'

'Waar than that!' says he. 'A lot waar than that! . . . I've lost my nowt!'

I could hardly believe my lugs. 'Lost yer nowt? Nivver!'

'Aye!' says he, 'I've lost my nowt! I got 40 beasts aff the Orkney boat yesterday, an' they were driven hame in floats an' putten into the coort for the nicht; young beasties, ye ken, still a bittie restless at bedtime, but that's normal aifter the voyage. They were aa keen eneuch for their mait, an' I thocht they wid be sattled doon afore mornin'. But, man, the shed's teem noo, an' we canna see them naewye. They're clean tint, man, clean tint! They've pickit a pint on the compass that naebody kens aboot, an' they could be far eneuch noo!'

Even my inexperienced ear could sense the deep anxiety in the poor man's voice, and I had enough sense to refrain from asking 'Fit feel left the door open?' But I did speir, 'Could ye use a compass, supposin' ye hid sic a thing?'

'No!' says he, 'I widna ken a compass fae a clock. It wis jist a thocht!'

'Weel!' says I. 'Ye're nae needin' a compass, for ye're facin' in the richt direction! There's aboot 40 young beasts on the lawn at the Big Hoose, some o' them near up to their bellies in't, an' it new laid anaa! They maan be strangers, for nae daicent Buchan beastie wid daar ging on till't. I ken the Mannie's awa for the day, so . . . at yer hardest, an' get them aff o't. An' shut the door iss time!'

Oh, the words, boys! Oh, the words! Even if I could spell them (and I couldna), the Buchanie widna print them (and it shouldna). Spik aboot fower letters? They came in aa shapes an' sizes, an' a hantle o' different colours, syne he wis awa like the clappers, aifter 'is nowt.

Me? I sat an' leuch, an' leuch, till there wis verra nearly a washin'. It wis richt sair, but I jist couldna help it!

Memory now takes me several years further back to a happier occasion. We were fishing off the Durham coast, and we had toiled all day for very little indeed. It was shift, shift, shift, seeking the elusive cod, but it wasn't till evening that we found them. Our last haul for the day was a bobby-dazzler, a great bag of prime quality fish. Oh, if only we had been here all day! Ye ken the wye o't. But it was too late. Just like Blockbusters, we would have to await Tuesday's edition.

Now it so happened that, as we were in the process of getting our great bag aboard, who should come sailing close past but Billy, one of the locals, an old friend and as colourful a character as I have ever met. He was close enough for direct speech, so there was no need for radio contact. In the gathering dark, while the two boats lay close together we hatched a little plot. When we got into harbour, neither of us would say boo! In the morning, both of use would hang back until the rest of the fleet had sailed, then we would come back to this happy spot and make a killing. Radio silence, of course.

As it happened, it was one of the 'best laid schemes' that didna ging agley. Tuesday was a memorable day, for the fish were awaiting us, and we spent the whole day with them. Very pleasant company they were too! Billy was never more than half a mile away, getting on just as well as we were. Solid stuff!

Now it was dark and we were headed for Shields; the lights on the Tyne piers were winking dead ahead, and the red flash of Soutar Point lighthouse was broad on the port beam. For some unknown reason it was clear as a bell that night; usually it was thick fog when we were seeking a landfall. The sea was like the proverbial millpond and the further outlook was not at all bad. Things could hardly be better! The awful rabble on the radio had slowly died away as boat after boat had ceased fishing and the skippers had gone below to their suppers. We were to have our supper in harbour, for the lads were still busy clearing the deck. That would be nice . . . the wings of small roker skate (wings the size of your hand had been hanging in the sun for a day or two) would be dipped in batter and fried in deep fat, with chips. Two huge enamel ashets would be required to contain the feast, and not a vestige would be left.

Then, across the miles of velvety darkness came the voice of Billy's son, calling his Dad on the radio, seeking information.

'You've been very quiet today, Dad!' It was more than half question.

'Well, son, you know how it is with all them Scotties around . . . ye cannot hear anybody for everybody!' True.!

'Where ye been fishin' today, Dad?'

'Oh, here and there, as usual. You know, shift, shift, shift!' Oh, the lees!

'There's nothing at all out here, Dad. Wondering if it's worth steaming shorewards during the night. Any fish gettin' in there?'

'Not a lot, as far as I've heard, but ye cannot believe them Scotties. Most of them are anointed liars.' I was enjoying the conversation. The son was probing, probing, and for want of a definite answer, he was suspicious.

'Have ye heard or seen Peter today, Dad? He's been very quiet too. He's a Scottie, but he'll tell the truth if you ask him.'

'Haven't seen hide or hair of Peter all day. Mebbe he's away home in disgust.'

'Peter doesn't go home when the weather and the tide are both favourable, and I'm sure he'll be wiggin (listening in) just now. I'll give him a shout, and get the low-down on inshore matters.'

But, before he had time to call me, his Dad made a colossal mistake ... he started singing into the mike, 'Keep yer feet still, Geordie hinney'. Now, that was a dead give-away, for not unless he was very happy did Billy sing on the radio, and not until he had a boat-load of fish was Billy really happy. So now the son's suspicions were certainties, and he would be steaming at full speed for inshore waters, some eight hours distant. Without doubt, he would join our little party in the morning.

When Billy had finished his excruciating solo, there came a verbal arrow from the son, 'Remember Georgie Washinton, Dad!' It took a second or two to spot the inference ... Georgie Washinton never told a lie.

'Sure, son, I remember Georgie Washinton all right!' Then he launched out on the second verse of his song.

When silence had been mercifully restored, there came yet another barb. 'Dad, I don't believe you know who Georgie Washinton was!'

'Oh, I know all about Georgie Washinton, son. He's the b----r that shot the apple off the other b-----r's head!'

Well done, Billy! I leuch till I was nae-weel. Feel aathegither? Aye, surely, but I did tell ye that some o' the words had mair than fower letters.

The Leaking Bog

There are farmers and farmers; there are fishermen and fishermen. They are not all the same. As a rule, the good fisherman keeps a tidy boat, just as the good farmer keeps a tidy place. Any sensible skipper, seeing that some part of his deck machinery is badly worn, will have the said part repaired or renewed as soon as possible, knowing full well that, should that part break while at sea, it could cost two or three days of fishing time. A less responsible fella will let the thing run until it breaks, in the hope that 'the insurance' will pay for the repair. Any farmer worth his salt will have his implements in perfect order long before the crop is ready; his less responsible oppo waits until the barley's cryin' oot to be cut before discovering that his combine harvester has somehow seized up! I've seen it all happen, and I'm sure that the Lord should have mentioned the men-folk in His parable of the foolish virgins!

I'll never forget the day I saw a great muckle combine comin' rummlin' doon a farm road to make the very first cut of the season. The open gate of the barley park was directly opposite the end of the farm road so, in a sudden fit of courtesy, I stopped my van and signed that he should cross my bows. This he proceeded to do, with a friendly wave of acknowledgement, but sink me if the monster didna stall, richt across the road, blocking baith lanes. And the reason? Nae fuel in the tank! Boys, ye nivver saw naething like yon! In twa meenits there wis fifty or sixty motorists, half a dizzen bobbies and twa fairmers, aa sweerin' blue lowes! Somebody ran back to the fairm to get a suppie diesel in a tin, only to discover that the fairm tunk wis eel (empty)! That fairly put the lid on't! Then somebody noticed that I was the ile man, so the hale jing-bang fell oot on me! It wis aa MY blame! I should ha' KENT, athoot bein' TELLT, that the tunk wis TEEM! I'm tellin' ye, I wis lucky to get oot o' yon wi' my life especially since I sat there lachin' like a tippeny bookie! I jist couldna help it. Naebody seemed to realise that I wis

Esso, and that farmer dealt wi' Shell! Every time the barley ripens, I mine on yon day! Feels were there in plenty, but nivver a virgin to be seen!

Could it be that such episodes are sent to cheer us on our way? Depends on how you look at them, I suppose, and no doubt it's a great help if you can find some innocent person on whom to lay the blame!

Another unforgettable incident took place one dark winter day, when I had just left the cattle mart at Maud to keep an appointment at Banff. The road was 'like a bottle' with ice, so driving was rather tricky. I had just reached yon fearsome bend on the Fedderate road when a Land-rover, coming from the opposite direction, came skidding across the road, 'Bowff' into my starboard side. Although both of us got a scare, there was very little damage to either vehicle. The other driver was Sandy Lee fae Forda-fourie, a first class fairmer and an eminent breeder of prize-winning sheep.

'Man!' say he. 'I'm richt gled I've met ye! Fadder tellt me this mornin' t' order ile for the central heatin'. He's needin' the stuff the day, cos the tunk's near teem! A boddy canna dee athoot heat in this widder, but I've clean forgotten t' phone the Broch for the ile. It's richt handy, meetin' ye like this! Will 'ee see aboot the order? That wid save me forgettin' again!'

'Aye, surely!' says I. 'But this winna be for Fyoordie's, yer ain place. I'll tell them it's for Kinbog, far yer father bides. I ken it's jist nae distance awa, but it'll save time if they ging t' the richt place for a start.'

'The verra dunt!' says he, and off he went to the sheep sales.

From a phone-box in Pitsligo, I called the Broch office with the order, stressing that it should be entered in block capitals to denote its urgency.

'Right-oh!' says the quine. 'I'm ready! Fire aheid! Faa is't for?'

'Lee, Kinbog,' says I. 'Twa hunner gallon heatin' ile. Urgent! Afore dark!'

'O.K., O.K.!' she says. 'Keep the heid!'

Now, then, fit did the great feel dee? She wrote the order in block capitals, aaricht, but she wrote 'LEAKIN' BOG'! I'm tellin' ye, it taks aa kinds!

When George Stephen, the lorry driver scanned the order book, he says, 'Far on earth did that order come fae?'

'Peter phoned it in!' says the quine. 'He says it's urgent! The folkies 'll be deid wi' caul if they dinna get the ile afore dark!'

'Aha!' says George. ''Twis Peter, wis't? Up t'is tricks again, eh? Jist wyte till I get a hud o' Peter! I'll seen sort HIM oot! He winna catch me wi' that kind o' nonsense! We hiv a Redbog, a Bluebog, a Whitebog an' a Blackbog on oor books, but a Leakinbog? Nivver! Peter should ha' phoned a plumber! Stroke oot the order. Ha, ha, ha!'

So Lee, Kinbog put a gey caal nicht ower 'is heid. An' faa div ye think got the blame? Muggins again! Fit sorra idder? I widna care, but George had been supplying Lee, Kinbog for years.

Apparently there's times that folk jist gings clean gyte! The barley 'll seen be ripe again, so keep yer peepers open! Ye nivver ken fit a boddy micht see or hear!

A Shot in the Dark

Peterhead's last rowing life-boat, the George Pickard, stood on her heavy carriage in the old Life-boat shed on that part of the quay which is known as the Green Hill. The shed, a sturdy granite building, stood gable-on to the quay, its rear gable the great storm-dyke which, in easterly storms could be overtopped by mountainous seas. From her station, the boat could be dragged to the most convenient slipway, so that she could leave the harbour by either the North or the South entrance. Very handy!

With the advent of motor Life-boats the present Life-boat shed was built, and the old boat and shed became surplus to requirements. But I remember clearly how, on Life-boat Day great horses dragged the George Pickard on her carriage through the streets of the town. Each Life-boatman, suitably and fully clad in oilskins and life-jacket was armed with a collection bag on the end of a long bamboo pole which could reach the farthest on-lookers. A great day, Life-boat Day, and oh, the horses were bonny!

Well, now, it came to pass that the George Pickard, with all her gear was purchased by Sandy Davidson (Dites) who had a coal-yard on the Seagate, in the days when it was quite common for folks to buy their coal one pail at a time. Sandy was a proper rough diamond, but he had no objection to us boys going to have a look at his boat, and how we marvelled at the 'holes in the fleer', for letting the water out, should any come on board. Sandy's first move was to have a twin-cylinder Bolinder engine (say 30 to 40 hp) installed in the old boat, then he got a set of trawl gear (tut-tut) and commenced poaching (again tut-tut).

Now, Sandy was not alone in this failing, for Peterhead men have always shown a marked propensity for poaching. I doubt if there's any part of the Scottish coast that hasn't been 'visited' by the P.D.s. Indeed, one irate skipper did approach a certain Admiral of the Fleet with the earnest request that he should 'stop his blasted sub-marines fae practisin' in yon Bey as lang as the cod wis on'. And yet another, who shares with me a common birthday, was once asked by his crew, 'Could ye nae shift aff a bittie, skipper, so's we can pee athoot folk lookin' at's?'

I'm sure the powers that be made a great mistake when they banned the use of the trawl inside the three-mile limit. Had they said, 'Thou shalt not trawl outside the three-mile line', then the grounds inside that line would have remained untouched, as they were originally meant to be. But then, the powers that be have never attained a Degree in Psychology.

Sandy had a great confederate in Partan Jake, skipper of the Water Lily another boat with a 'boom-boom' engine. The pair of them would go trawling as bold as brass in the Cample (atween Rattray Head and Cairnbulg Briggs) and in Broch Bey. Of course they showed no lights, but a boddy could easy hear the boom-boom as far as Mormond

Hill. Spik aboot ostriches! The smaa-boat men in St Combs, Inverallochy and Cairnbulg turned a blind eye to the raiders as long as their own 'troonks' remained un-disturbed. Queer folk, yon. They say 'troonks' instead o' 'creels', they say 'pairk' for park, 'bate' for boat, and 'most' for mast. Still, I'm come o' yon 'fyolk', so I'd better hud my tongue.

Ye see, it's them that's richt an' hiz that's vrang, for they've held on to their ain tongue, far we've thrown maist o' oors awa. Theirs is the richt fisher tongue, an' lang may they keep it.

Noo, far wis I? Oh, aye, I mine noo; Sandy Dites an' Partan Jake poachin' in the Cample on a richt bonny nicht; nae a funk o' win', an' jist a wee bittie o' easterly lift. Hazy kine? Weel, aye, jist a thochtie. For a crew, Jake had his twa breethers, the Yunk (cos he had been in the States) and Twinkletoes (cos he had been as pirn-taed as a doo aa his days). Sandy had jist the ae man, Brucie, anither rough diamond, nae that ony o' the squad wis ony better. They wid ha' made a rare diamond bracelet, I'm sure!

There wis nae sign o' the 'catcher', an' the twa boaties wis deein' awa gran', fin doon comes the fog as thick as a blunkit. Problems? Oh, aye, problems! Nae radar, nae wireless, nae naething, ye see! But things like that disna bother a P.D. poacher, so Jake heaves up his gear an' scutters aboot in the fog till he gets a hud o' Sandy. Syne, abeen the boom-boom o' the twa engines, he roars.

'We'll ging into the Broch Bey, an' leave this place t' you. That wye we winna come foul o' een anither.'

'Please yersel',' cries Sandy, 'but ye'd better watch the rocks at the Bick'n (the Beacon on Cairnbulg Briggs). It'll seen be low water, an' it's the tap o' the stream tide, so there winna be a lot o' watter. Ye canna thole t' be ower far in at the Bick'n, ye ken! Ye winna see the licht far the nicht, freen!'

'I ken aa that, Sandy. I'll watch!' says Jake. But he didna watch. The first he kent wis 'Bumpity-bump', an' the Water-lily wis hard fast amon' tangles. Full speed astarn made nae difference; she wis fair stuck.

Now, to be on a boat which is fast by the heel in a moderate swell can be a salutory experience, for the boat will twist and roll in torment, seeking the freedom of her natural element. There is nothing natural about the roll; it

88

is more of a lurch, as she lays first one side, then the other deep in the water, with a vicious, twisting motion which always ends in a sudden jerk. In Jake's own words, 'It gars ye feel as if yer doup's aafa yokie'.

Naebody on the shore wid hear them shoutin' so they wid fire a rocket, but there wisna sic a thing in the boat. Weel, they wid licht a flare, but fit wid they burn? An' faa wid see't on a nicht like this, onywye? Still, they wid hae t' dee something, so they trailed an aul strae matrass oot o' the caibin, soakit it wi' diesel an' set fire till't. Od, boys! Sic a bleeze; they verra near set the boat on fire!

Now, Sandy, in the aul Life-boat thocht it wis time he kent richt jist far he wis, so him an' Brucie gets the trawl aboard wi' a fine haulie o' flukes.

'This thickness is jist nae mowse!' says Sandy. 'We'd better try an' get a hud o' something so's we can get oor bearin's. Lat's hae a look for the Bick'n. It canna be that far awa.'

'I thocht I saw a searchlight eyvnoo!' says Brucie. 'Maybe it's the catcher!'

'Nae fears,' says Sandy, 'the catcher winna come in here on a nicht like this! It widna been the Licht, wid it?'

'Na! Twis ower low for that. I've lost it again, onywye. I winner foo yon mob's gettin' on in the Broch Bey.'

'We'll creep in a bittie an' hae a look,' says Sandy. 'Fog an' daylicht's bad aneuch, but fog an' darkness is hell an' aathegither. Keep yer een skint for a licht o' ony kind.'

As it happened, the first licht they saw wis the bleeze o' the matrass on the Water Lily's deck, a glare that shone on the dark broon tangles that jist broke the screeth (surface) o' the water. There seemed, however, to be a clear channel jist astarn o' the Water Lily.

Sandy had the situation sized up in a tick, an' he wisna slow to tell Jake aa aboot it.

'For ony sake pit oot that blasted bonfire, Jake, or ye'll hae the hale North Sea alairmed! It seems ye've geen up a trink (trench) amon' the rocks. I'll ging oot a bittie an' turn, syne I'll come in starn first an' get a rope across t' ye. I'll get a better rug at ye if I'm gaun aheid.'

So Sandy came dead slow astarn into the trink, canny, canny. Then, at a reasonable distance from the casualty, he stopped his boat.

'Ye'll hae t' come closer than that,' cries Jake. 'Faa div ye think's gaun t' fire a rope that distance?'

'Nae dam fears,' says Sandy, 'we'll gie ye a heavin' line, an' ye can mak' it fast t' yer tow-rope. Stand by!'

Enter Brucie, Lifeboat-man supreme, an expert with the heaving-line. The line in question had on its end a foot-long length of bamboo, and on the end of that a lump o' leed as big as yer niv (fist). A deadly missile indeed, capable of being thrown an amazing distance by a practised hand.

'Ye'd better hap yer heids,' cries Brucie, 'or I'll brain the lot o' ye. Fussle fin ye're ready.'

Partan Jake an' the Yunk immediately dived into the hold, but Twinkletoes took to the wheelhoose an' cooried doon on the fleer. He had only been there half-a-meenit fin he thocht he wid be safer in the hold. He wis half-roads there fin Jake fusselt, an' he wis jist abriest o' the hatch fin the leed, slung by the mighty arm o' Brucie got him 'Bowff' on the heid. Oh, the peer Twinkle!

He fell doon the hole like a ton o' coal on tap o' his twa breethers. Syne they fell oot on him an' kickit him half to death for giein' them sic a scare. Breethers dis things like that, sometimes.

Finally, the Water Lily was successfully refloated and made her home port under her own steam and with no apparent damage. Not so, the peer Twinkle; he nott sax stitches at the back o' 'is lug, an' some strappin' for 'is ribs.

Brucie's verdict on the hale affair?

'Weel!' says he, modestly. 'Twinkle should be thankfu' gled it wis pick dark, an' smore thick. Itherwise I wid ha' killt 'im!'

The Clootie Dumplin'

Once more the good ship Meadowsweet was homeward bound from the West-coast fishing grounds. After an unusually early homecoming from East Anglia, the Turk had wasted no time; three days at home, then it was away again to the Minch. Now it was getting on for Christmas, time to go home for a whilie. And, as Jeemsie said, 'sax or saiven wiks in the Minch wis lang eneuch for onybody, specially in the winter-time'.

If these were the Turks sentiments, he certainly didn't express them. Early that morning, while his crew, unnaturally silent, had hauled a fleet of empty nets the skipper had simply remarked, 'Queer, cappernyaam craiters, the herrin'. They like the moon at Yarmooth, but they dinna like it roon' here'. If he heard Jeemsie mutter, 'They're nae the only eens!' he paid no attention but, when he himself said, 'I think we'll awa hame', he couldna fail to notice the marked increase in the speed of the hauling process. Crews speak loudest when they are silent.

On the way north towards Cape Wrath, the Turk drew Jeemsie's attention to the stark beauty of the snow-covered massifs of Arkle, Foinaven and Stack.

'That's far Suntie Claa bides.' But Jeemsie showed little interest.

'I can see the Isle o' Lewis fae here, skipper,' says he.

'Oh aye, Jeemsie, that's a sure sign that it's gaan t' be rain!'

'An' fit dis't mean fin ye canna see't fae here, skipper?'

'Oh!' says the Turk. 'That means that it's rainin' already!'

But there was no rain. While the shippie steamed steadily eastward along the North coast, the weather remained bright and clear. Meanwhile the crew busied themselves among the nets, 'makkin' them up' (making of each net an individual bundle). When this job was finished, the side-decks were filled with neatly bundled nets.

'Now,' says the Turk, 'pit them below, an' pit the hatches on, we've a lang road aheid o's yet, an' it's winter-time. Better safe than sorry!'

Thereafter it was 'Set the watch', and those who were off duty could sleep, or read, or jist sit and news. As they drew steadily nearer to the Pentland Firth the Turk consulted his tide-table and discovered what he already knew; they had missed the tide at the Firth.

'It's jist a waste o' time an' coal tryin' t' steam throwe that Firth against the ebb. She jist winna dee't, so we'll jist hae an 'oor or twa in Scrabster till the tide rins ower. It's mair than likely we'll hae company there, onywye.'

As the Turk had expected, there were already two or three drifters in Scrabster basin, lying at the pier which was built of great flat slabs of slate laid on top of each other, without any mortar. It was common practice for fishing boats to lie for a few hours in Scrabster when the ebb tide in the Pentland Firth hindered their passage west to east. Bigger vessels would lie in Scrabster Bay. For vessels bound east to west against the flood tide, Sinclair Bay, just north of Wick was the waiting-point. The tides in the Firth are so fierce that only very fast ships can master them, and to tackle the Firth at all, when wind and tide are in opposite directions is to ask for a double helping of trouble, for then the sea becomes like a raging beast.

It was much too cold to go ashore, so the fishermen sat in each other's cabins or toasted themselves on each other's fiddleys, discussing the depressed state of their industry and the even more depressing threat of war. Only Duncan ventured ashore, returning very shortly with a day-old newspaper.

'Onything new in the paperie the day, Duncan?' says the Turk.

'Nae a great lot,' says Duncan. 'I dinna think iss mannie Chamberlain's gettin' on verra sair wi' Hitler, but I see a lad in Foggieloan's gotten a snake for a pet!'

'A snake!' says Jeemsie. 'Gyaad sake, he canna be richt! A snake by onything! Div ye ken onything aboot snakes, skipper?'

'Weel awyte! Fine div I ken aboot snakes, my loon. Mony a scare hiv I gotten wi' the brutes.'

'I didna ken ye wis oot in the jungle, skipper! Wis ye in Africa?'

'Africa?' says the Turk. 'Africa. Nivver een! I wis on the island o' Raasay. Hiv ye nivver seen a Raasay snake? No? Weel, ye're nae missin' naething, for they're jist nae mowse! They're nae gweed t' get clear o', cos they pit their tails in their mous an' come rowlin' aifter ye like a gird!'

Duncan and Jeemsie looked into each other's faces, but made no comment. They had never been ashore on Raasay, and they kent naething aboot snakes. Still! Wi' the skipper, ye could nivver be sure!

'I hiv a dog at hame,' says Duncan, 'but I dinna think I could thole t' hae a snake aboot the hoose ava. I dinna like creepy things.'

'I'm readin' a bookie eyvnoo aboot a loon that got wannert in the Brazilian jungle wi 's chum,' says Jeemsie. 'They saw a giant snake that could swally a coo. I think it wis an anaconda, or something lik' 'at.'

'That'll be Martin Rattler that ye're readin' aboot,' says the skipper. 'I'm surprised that he's still on the go, cos he wis at the same game fin I wis a loon. He maun be an aul mannie noo!'

Jeemsie smiled, then queried, 'Ye dinna hae nae pets yersel', skipper?'

'Me? No!' says the Turk. 'But there wis a time fin I had a monkey. Fin I wis a loon, ye ken.'

'Did ye get that on Raasay, amon' the snakes, skipper?'

'Na, my loon, there's nae monkeys on Raasay. I got the monkey fin I wis in Mogadishu on a cargie-boat. Aa the wye fae Montrose wi' ten thoosan' ton o' tattie seeds.'

'Tattie seeds?' says Duncan. 'Tattie seeds? Div ye nae mean seed tatties?'

'Tattie seeds, Duncan. In packeties, ye ken, jist like ither seeds.'

'Aye, aye, skipper, tattie seeds it is! Noo lat's hear aboot the monkey!'

'Weel,' says the Turk, 'I bocht the monkey fae a hawker mannie. He tellt me it wis a spikkin' monkey, the only een o' its kine in the world. An' he wis richt aboot that.'

'A spikkin' monkey? Fit did she say, skipper? says Jeemsie in astonishment.

'Och! She didna say an aafa lot, Jeemsie, but ilkie time she made a mess on the table, she said, "That remains t' be seen!" We wis jist half-wye hame fin the skipper fun oot that I had a monkey aboord an' he gid reid mad. Man,

he took the monkey b' the tail an' haived her ower the side, the coorse chiel. I grat for a fyle, cos I wis jist a loon, an' I lay waakened, listenin' t' the beat o' the propeller in the watter. She wis an aul-fashioned ship, ye ken; fin she wis licht, half o' the propeller wis oot o' the watter, an' it made a queer kine o' soon, flap-flap-flap, aa the time. But I seen forgot the peer monkey.'

'It wisna richt t' droon the craiter,' says Jeemsie.

'A coorse man, yon skipper, Jeemsie. I hope ye appreciate the skipper ye hiv aboord here.'

'Nivver mine that,' says Jeemsie. 'Can monkeys sweem?'

'Not a stroke!' says the Turk. 'They're terrified at watter!'

'Oh!' says Jeemsie. 'I wis jist winnerin'.'

'Ye'll hardly believe this, Jeemsie, but fin we gid back t' Montrose for mair tattie seeds' . . .

'Seed tatties, skipper, seed tatties!' interrupted Duncan.

'Nivver mind that, Duncan, but we got in past Scurdy Ness, an' fin we wis passin' Ferryden (ye ken, yon placie far the wifies' claes-poles is sometimes in the sea), aa the folk wis shoutin', an' pointin' at the ship's starn, so the skipper gart me ging aift t' see fit wis adee. Od! Fin I lookit ower the starn, here wis the monkey, jumpin' fae blade to blade o' the propeller t' keep hersel' oot o' the watter! Three solid wiks she had been deein that. Clivver monkey!'

'I hardly think that's true, skipper,' says Duncan. 'Fit wye did she nae shout for help? Ye did say she wis a spikkin' monkey!'

They all had a good lach, and the story session ended. On the very last of the ebb, the Meadowsweet nosed her way through the Firth, scraping close round the corner at Duncansby Head, so close that Jeemsie could reach out with an oar from the sma'-boat, and touch the very cliff.

'The skipper maybe disna ken aboot seed tatties,' says Duncan, 'but he fairly kens this Firth!'

Late forenoon found our heroes well across the Moray Firth, with Mormond high on the starboard bow.

'Hey, Chef!' says Duncan. 'Seein' that this 'll be oor last denner aboord the ship for this year, an' seein' that it's near Christmas, fit aboot a duff?'

'That wid be fine,' says Jeemsie, 'but I dinna think there's as muckle stuff left as wid mak' a duff o' ony size. I didna stock up this wik in Stornowa', cos I expectit this wid be oor hinmist wik awa'. See fit ye can rake oot o' the locker, an' ye can hae a go at a duff if ye like. There's a fine pot o' broth soossin' awa', here!'

Duncan didna get a great lot o' stuff in the locker, but there wis at least some!

'Jeemsie, my loon!' says he. 'There's hardly aneuch t' mak' a big duff, but I think I could mak' a clootie dumplin' wi' this lot. It wid be fine an' Christmas-like, an' we'd aa get a bittie. I'm a don han' at clootie dumplins!'

'Fire aheid, Duncan!' says Jeemsie. 'But for God's sake dinna mak the thing on the same scale as ye did wi' the custard, else we'll aa be smored!'

So Duncan got goin', an' the bonny dumplin' wis plunkit into the pot.

When dinner-time came, Jeemsie handed the great muckle pot doon the trap to Duncan.

'Ye can dish up if ye like, Duncan. I'll be doon in a couple o' shakes.' Then Jeemsie stoked up the stove and saw that everything was in order, but when he went down into the cabin, he got a shock. There was no sign of the dumplin'.

'Ye've aa been in a fearsome hurry, surely. Ye micht ha' kept a bittie dumplin' t' me, Duncan!'

There was no answer. Aabody jist kept suppin' awa at their broth, nae even liftin' a heid. Jeemsie kent there wis something far wrang fin Duncan had negleckit his chum.

'Fa scoffed the dumplin'? Come awa noo! Fa gluffed it!' No reply!

'Aa richt, than, aa richt, dinna tell me! But the least ye can dee is t' gimme back the cloot it wis in!'

'Good grief!' cries the Turk, turnin' green. 'Wis there a cloot on't?'

The Rim Net

It's most unlikely that you've ever seen a rim net, for such contraptions are not exactly common in this enlightened age. In fact, any one of today's fishermen would look at you in amazement were you to mention such a thing. I'm sure the rim net is a relic of the days before the Flood, when Tubal-cain was the instructer of every artificer in brass and iron (Genesis 4:22).

'Aha',' says you. 'Fit on earth has brass or iron t' dee wi' a net?' Well, it's like this, ye see! The rim net needs iron, for it's jist like a bairn's gird (hoop), except that it's in twa halfs, hinged in the middle. A circular piece of netting is woven onto the iron rim and, apart from a rope closing the trap, the outfit is complete. Sorry! I'm forgetting the bait! Bait for a net? Aye; bait for a net! Ye tie bitties o' bait into the net and lower the hale apothick into the water. It's best to let the net sink right to the bottom, where the two halves of the rim open out and the baited net lies flat. At any time that you so desire, you can tit the towie and close the trap. If you're lucky, you may capture any fish which

have gathered to 'hose' at the bait. Perhaps I should stress that this is definitely not the easiest way to make a living, but I'm sure you're welcome to try.

In the days of my youth, there were a few worthy exponents of the noble art of rim netting. These worthies invariably fished during the famine months of winter, when a puckly o' podlies might realise a few coppers. And, since any bait available at that time of year was almost certain to be rotten to the point of decomposition, there was about these characters an unmistakable odour. Oh, boys! What a guff! Much, much worse than somebody opening their hand-bag!

So much for the rim net, but thereby hangs a tale.

It was spring-time, about twelve years ago, when I was still employed as a Traffic Controller in the control tower at Peterhead Harbour. Those were the days when pipe-laying barges, with their great retinues of attendant vessels were very much to the fore. Indeed, the Bay could scarcely cope with the number of vessels requiring its use, so much so that supply boats had to anchor in tiers of eight or ten and, even at that, many ships had to lie outside. The great Oil Boom was in top gear. There was also the expected influx of certain ladies whose morals were exactly on par with those of the men who sought their company. But that is just by the way.

It had been a beautiful day, and I was thinking it was about time that I was getting my boatie ready for a go at the ripper. You see, if you intend to salt and dry some fish, so that you may have 'hairy tatties' in the winter time, it's best to get the job done in Spring, afore the great foosty bluebottles comes on the scene. So it was with such thoughts in mind that I went to get my converted ship's-lifeboat ready for action. Oh, boys, what a mess she was in! Jist fair clartit wi' fool black ile, like aa the ither smaa-boats.

At that time, the water in the inner basins of the harbours was covered with a thick scum of black sump oil, the stuff the farmers call 'burssen ile'. Since the North entrance had been closed, there was no flow of clean water through the harbour, so the oil lay trapped, and every rise and fall of the tide set a fresh layer of filthy grease on slipways, ladders and mooring ropes. It was utterly impossible to keep a boatie clean. The place was an affront to any modern society, but when I made verbal complaint, I was told that 'Where there's muck, there's brass'. A letter in the local paper, with my signature, got me into very bad odour for a whilie, very nearly as bad as the guff of the rim net men. You see, I used the unpardonable word 'cesspool', the politest word I could think of at the time. Worst of all, I think, nobody seemed to think of the potential fire risk. Still, that has all been remedied by the installing of clean-water ducts, and the place is much cleaner.

Well, now, on the evening in question, I decided to take the boat into the Bay to give the engine a good run, and I had just got the engine started when my seven year old grandson, Peter appeared on the scene. Of course, he wanted a sail in the boat and would brook no denial despite my warning that he would probably get his clothing in a mess. So, with the youngster at the helm, we set out.

It was great fun for the loon, steering the boat round and round among the tiers of anchored ships. He was as proud as a peacock when some of the seamen gave him a cheery wave, and I had some difficulty persuading him that it was time to go home. We were actually making for the harbour when a great muckle ocean-going tug began to hoot-hoot on her compressed-air horn, apparently to draw our attention. Urgent hand-signals from the tug's bridge conveyed the message that our services were required, so I drew my boatie alongside.

It transpired that the skipper had just been informed by radio that the tug's services would not be required that night, so he was at liberty to let his crew have a few hours of shore leave. Would I take some of the lads ashore? I would, of course, be rewarded, and they would find their own way back.

'Aye, surely!' says I. 'I'll wait till ye get your go-ashores on. There's nae hurry, and in the meantime I'll try to get the boat cleaned up a bittie. She's far ower fool for passengers!'

Peter disappeared aboard the tug to have a tour of inspection, while I tried to remove the worst of the oily filth from the seats in my boatie. My labours were in vain, for salt water and a broom are useless against oil. I was about to give up in despair when a quiet voice said, 'Would you like some hot water?', and the tug's cook passed me the end of a stout rubber hose. 'Just open the nozzle when you want hot water, and here's a bucket of detergent!' Boys, in a few minutes, ye couldna see the boatie for steam, and she was cleaner than she had been for years. What a transformation! Then the shore party appeared on deck, rarin' to go.

'Hold on!' says I. 'Far's the loon?' At that very moment Peter appeared carrying a bunch of some forty bananas and two tins of Coke. He spurned all offers of assistance with his prize. Were we ready to go now? Apparently not, for one of the party wasn't quite ready yet.

While we awaited the latecomer, the skipper says, 'Nice little boat you've got here! Would you like some paint for her?'

'Aye, surely!' says I, and was promptly presented with a five-gallon drum of International white enamel. That was worth a bob or twa, eh? They say that 'a gaan fitt's aye gettin'!'

Apparently the latecomer was still not ready, so I had a look at a little group of seamen who were fishing from the stern of the tug. They seemed to me to be Spaniards although, mind you, I could have been mistaken. Only the officers, all Americans, were being allowed ashore, but the little group of fishers didn't seem to care. Boys! I could scarcely believe my eyes when I saw that they were using a rim net! And they were fishing for crabs, not the big partans which are so popular with gourmets, but the little green 'craibs' which are to be found in the rock pools along the shore. How these fellas seemed to relish the craibs which we used to call 'grindies', or 'grindie-tochers'. They were 'sookin' the taes' with great gusto!

'Oh, gyaad!' says I, then I got an even bigger shock, for the bait in their prehistoric net consisted of five lovely pork chops! Judging by the number of crabs in the net, pork was a highly successful bait, though the seamen themselves wouldn't eat it. I thought it was a shameful waste of good food.

Well, now, when we finally did get home, I teased Peter about the bananas.

'Hey!' says I. 'Fit aboot the boat's share? Div ye nae think that I'm entitled t' half o' the bananas, seein' that the boat's mine?'

My hints fell on remarkably stony ground, and I laughed as I watched him stagger up the road with his load. On no account would he accept assistance. Alone I did it!

When I was stowing my own prize in the sheddie, the wife looks oot, an' she says, 'Fit on earth's 'at ye hiv in the tin?'

'Woman!' says I. 'That's a five-gallon drum o' first-class, top-notch, International fite enamel!'

'Nae bad!' says she. 'But could ye nae ha' gotten a brush anaa, eence ye wis at it?'

Some folk's nivver pleased!

The Gold Rush

Do you think you could forget your car for a whilie and transform yourself into a pedestrian? You do? Well, take the South Road at the Kirkburn Mill (the Oo Mull) and head for the Cottage Hospital, keeping to the right-hand pavement, and close to the Mill dyke. You know, there used to be a hole in that dyke, a very special hole, for through it a bairn could look down into a rather mysterious courtyard, where the Kirk Burn appeared very briefly before disappearing under the road, to re-appear almost at sea level, pouring through two great massive iron pipes onto the stony foreshore. Ye needna bother lookin' for that hole noo, cos it's nae there! What a shame!

But nivver mind the hole in the dyke ... Far's the Burn? Fit on earth hiv they deen wi' the burn that eesed t' be the boundary o' the toon? I've lookit sair for't but I canna see't. Maybe it wis nivver the official boundary, but it wis certainly the boundary the time o' the Plague. If a mither wanted her bairn baptised, she wid stand on the toon side o' the burn an' hud her bairn abeen the watter,

so that the Minister on the ither bank could perform the ceremony. Country folk wid bring tatties an' vegetables and pedlars wid bring their wares, but cross the burn they wid not. The verra siller for ony transack had to be heated reid-het on a shovel afore it crossed the watter! Naebody in, an' naebody oot, that wis the rule. Lang afore my time!

Now, pedestrian, carry on, past the Kirkyaird till ye come to the twa hillocks on the Links. They're supposed to be burial mounds, but I'm sure I would nivver think aboot investigating. I'll jist tak their word for that! But, jist afore ye reach the hillocks, ye'll see a bonny flat bittie on the Links, far the Mission held an Open-air if it wis a bonny Sunday. A great place for fitba'; the genuine, original, identical spot far the Gold Rush began! Ye nivver heard o' the Gold Rush? Od, ye're richt ignorant! But, mind ye, there's a lot o' folk disna ken aboot it!

It all happened on a bonny summer day in the late twenties. On the fine flat bittie I've mentioned, a bourachie o' loons were playin' fitba', when a Grimsby liner entered the Bay, tooin' like murder. A 'liner' is a vessel which fishes with lines, just as a trawler uses a trawl. See? the two vessels may be otherwise alike.

Now, this was the Juliana, from Grimsby, calling in for a supply of bait before proceeding to far Northern waters.

Very soon we would see the Moozies' boatie, the Breadwinner leave the harbour with some 10 crans of herring in boxes, bait for the 'Grimmy'. This was a common event, the old Huxley being the most regular caller. Well, now, since the ba' wis bust, we gave up our game and crossed the road to watch the proceedings. No need whatsoever to watch the traffic. What was traffic? Once across the road, we settled down on the grass at the top of the cliff. It was actually a cliff, sheer to the beach, for the terraced paths to the Lido did not exist at that time. The cliff face was simply formed of earth, very dangerous indeed, although we didn't realise it.

Suddenly, the cliff top gave way beneath our weight, and the whole shebang went down like an avalanche. We were indeed fortunate not to be buried alive, for several tons of soil fell to the beach. After a quick count of heads we were able to reassure the few onlookers that nobody was missing, and we were still marvelling at our good fortune when a loon on a message bike said . . . 'Dis you lads ken that Tarzan or Nelson fun a twa-shillin' bit at the Diggin's the day?'

I'm tellin' ye, the Gold Rush was on! Twa shillins? A fortin, a Klondyke! Along the Embankment we ran, like a stampede of buffaloes, never doubting the truth of what we had heard. It had to be true, for we had gotten the actual name of the prospector who had made the lucky strike! Twa shillins, b' jingers. Twa hale shillins! What a rush, boys, what a rush. Those in front cried 'Forward', while those behind cried 'Wyte'.

Ower the Queenie Brig we panted, nae a loon in sicht. Great! We would still be in time. Up Castle Street then first left for the Diggins, the Municipal Dump, which burned like the fires of Hell and stank to high heaven. Boys, what a stammagaster we got! There wis aboot twa hunner loons there afore's. So we had been the last to hear the news. What a shame! There were loons there fae Queen Street an' Landale Road an' the Win'mill Brae, gran' loons that didna usually come near the Diggins, but

twa shillins wis twa shillins! Some siller, yon! It's a winner the Provost wisna doon. Maybe he wis, though I didna see him!

We rakit wi' sticks among the rubbish till the rising tide drove us out. Not a maik, boys, not a maik! Which goes to prove that being on the right spot at the right time is all important, in most walks of life.

For many generations the town's refuse was dumped into the top of a creek or gully among the rocks. The mouth of the gully, the Peel (Pool) was a favourite fishing place for the loons. Solid podleys, boys! Big saithes anaa! Jist sit here a whilie catchin' podleys, an' ye'll ging hame stinkin'.

The tide at high water lapped the lower parts of the great heap of corruption, but the upper parts smouldered continually, the acrid smell reaching all parts of the town, according as the winds dictated. What a guff, at times. Only a severe easterly gale would clean the gully completely; thereafter it simply filled up again. It's only about 15 years ago that the Diggins was forbidden territory, and the Scaffies took the rubbish elsewhere.

This fiery furnace, this temple of dangerous fumes was never without its regular worshippers. There were those who were there daily, scraping and raking with sticks for any item that could possibly sell, and wending their homeward way with a pathetic little baggie of 'something'. You'll see some folk on TV at the same caper in the big cities. Along with most of my playmates, I had a go at it more than once, till I got a sair skin fae my mither for my pains. That was all I ever got.

Amongst the great heaps of aise (ashes) and caff (corn chaff) and rotten fruit and all sorts of everything, there was always a proliferation of little jars, mostly ornamental, and usually very heavy. These were the Vaseline jars, and the cold-cream jars (Pond's?) and, (I think) some were marked Icilma. There were others which apparently had contained Vanishing Cream, a product which young ladies in a certain condition were said to rub on their tummies in some sort of forlorn hope.

Those were the days when each household had its 'orra pail' (usually plural) at the edge of the pavement on scaffie day. But many households had another pail for 'sweel', kitchen waste like tattie peelin's and neep skins, which was collected twice weekly by two inmates of the

Parish Home to feed the pigs which were kept on the site of the present Fire Station, where there was a vegetable garden. The 'mannies' came round with a pony and cairtie.

Now those days are long gone, but there are two questions which bother me. The first one is 'Far will they pit the stuff fin they rin oot o' quarries?'

The second has come to mind repeatedly over the years . . . 'What poor woman searched diligently, yet fruitlessly for the lost coin? Twa hale shillin's (10p)!

Did We Get Duff?

The wind was little more than a draught, but it was razor sharp. In the gutter, there was a hint of a frosty glitter, and the fitful blinking of the gas lamp-post merely served to make the darkness seem even blacker. All day long, the north-easterly swell had been increasing, until now, in the early evening, the dull sound of the breakers among the rocks had reached a crescendo, more of a snarl than a roar.

Beneath the lamp-post, a small group of fishermen were pacing to and fro, quietly discussing the parlous state of their industry.

'A gey heavy swaal, that! I dinna like the soun' o't!' says Partan Jake. 'There's nae win' for sic a sea!'

'That's the dog afore 'is maister! Ye'll get plenty o' win' the morn. Aye! An' mebbe afore the morn!' says Sheetlin.

'It winna bother neen o' hiz, I'm sure! We're aa ashore for a fyle, b' the look o't!' says Cork.

'I'm thinkin' I'm ashore for keeps! I'm nae gaan back! I've been a feel ower lang!' says Pun. 'I'm hame fae Yarmouth, an' instead o' gettin' a square-up, I'm tellt that I'm in debt! The skipper says I'm owe him fower powen for my grub! There's nae feels on God's earth like hiz hired men!'

Such heresy, so forcibly expressed, seemed to shock Pun's friends, for they ceased their pacing for a moment, to gaze at him as if he were a freak. This was somethng revolutionary!

'It's teen ye a lang time t' see the licht!' says Ora, the oldest man present. 'It's been on my mind for years, but I've aye been feart t' spik! I think it's time we gid on strike! The miners aye gets something wi' a strike! Could we nae dee the same?'

'Hear, hear! Cairry on, Ora!' says Sheetlin.

By this time, the company had doubled, and the word 'strike' was being used as if it were something reid het! When Ora spoke, they listened intently, nodding occasionally in agreement.

'Noo, boys, we're aa hired men (deck-hands) here the nicht. We dinna get wages, so we canna stump a card. THEREFORE, we canna get nae buroo, and THEREFORE, we hiv t' live on tick for the hale winter! I canna look the grocer in the face! I shot a wye (a type of gull), this mornin', an' that wis oor denner. I wis doon among the rocks at low water for a partan t' wir supper, an' god knows fit we'll dee the morn. I'm tellin' ye, lads, my bairns gings oot t' the water-closet, jist t' gar ither folk think they're gettin' mait!' At this there was a subdued laugh. A proper master of the colourful phrase, was Ora! But every man there knew that Ora was simply stating the stark facts of life.

Jeemsie, witless breet, opened his big mou' to venture an opinion, but Sheetlin turned on him like a serpent. 'Jist ee shut yer face, Jeemsie! Ye're a cook, on wages, so ye get the buroo! There's naething comin' ower you! This is a hired-man's pie, so ye'd better clear oot!' Jeemsie bolted!

Ora continued with his harangue. 'Boys! We wid aa be far better aff, workin' on the roads! The peer folkies in the Parish Home's a lot better aff than hiz. We'll hae t' get wages o' some kind!'

'Faar fae?' says Cork. 'The skippers an' owners disna hae the siller t' pey wages! So they tell me, onywye!'

'Dinna be daft!' says Ora. 'Maist o' them has hooses, an' ye can aye raise the win' on the strength o' a hoose! There's hardly a hoose in the toon but fit has a bond on't (mortgage). But hiz? We're expectit t' tar the rope, an' paint the bowse (floats), an' rig oot the ship, for naething! Jist t' keep yer berth. An' fit's yer berth worth?'

'Nae a dam' thing!' came the reply.

These were the deplorable conditions which drove so many herring fishermen to seek berths in the trawlers at Aberdeen. There they could get a wage plus a bonus, and, although the working conditions were atrocious, the poor 'herring-scalers' were glad of the money. Among the traditional fisher folk, the key-word was 'famine', a word whose meaning is completely lost on today's generation. The following year, the deckies refused to go to sea until they were guaranteed fifteen shillings (75p) per week! They got it, after a struggle.

Many of these men are still around today, and they find it passing strange that their tales of byegone days are dismissed by the younger generation as a parcel of lies. In a way this is understandable, for it must be difficult for a modern crew to grasp that what they pay for one week's grub, would have paid a drifter's coal-bill for a whole season. It is almost impossible to convince a young fisher that, after only one good trip, he can take home more money than his grandad could earn in five years.

Well, now, our Parliament at the end of the street had decided that they would require a democratically elected Strike Committee, when Pun says, 'Boys, I'll hae t' leave ye. There's a mairrige on in the Polar Hall the nicht, an' there's a cousin o' mine fae Portsoy at it. He canna come here fae Portsoy an' ging hame the same day, so he's bidin' wi' hiz for the nicht. He's likely in the hoose noo, so I'll hae t' ging hame an' spik till 'im. Pit me doon for the Comatee, if ye like'.

Pun had a mere fifty yards to cover to reach his hoosie, and, as he slipped quietly in at the front door, he saw a wondrous sight! Through the half-open door of the butt end (the kitchen/living room), he could see his cousin, in his Sunday best, sittin' in Pun's cheer, proclaimin' to Pun's bairns the wonders of the wedding feast. The bairns sat open-mou'ed an' goggle-e'ed at the fantastic fairytale that this gran' man wis tellin'.

'Oh! Sic a rare feed we got!' says he. 'First ava we got broth, syne we got beef an' tatties wi' neeps! An' we got duff, forbye, syne we feenished up wi' trifle! Wyte a meenit, noo! Did we get duff? No! We didna get duff! Hold on! I'm wrang! We did get duff! I mine noo! We could get a slice o' duff among the broth, or we could tak' it along wi' the beef an' tatties. Oh, aye! We got duff aa richt!

This got the better o' Pun, stannin' there in the dark lobby, wi' the slivver rinnin' ower his chin! Dinna forget that Pun wis a gey hungry chiel!

Then, alas, Pun did an aafa silly thing ... he slippit oot, the wye he had come in, an' made a bee-line for the West-end Bar, where he consumed a quantity of spirits. On tick! Nae a lot, mind ye, but then, he didna need a lot on a teem stammick, aifter a lang time athoot a dram ava!

Half an hour later, the newly formed Strike Committee heard a most peculiar noise above the roar of the swell. 'Twas the voice of their freen, Pun, comin' rollin' home through the raivelt hooses, nae carin' aboot the linth o' the street, but gey sair made at the breadth o't.

We'll hae t' see this!' says Ora, so the Comatee moved in a body, in the direction of the strident orator who was clinging to a lamp-post, less than twenty yards fae his ain door, proclaimin' to the world at large ...

'Did we get duff? ... NO! WE DIDNA GET DUFF!'

'Did we get duff? ... AYE! WE GOT DUFF!'

'Wis the duff among the broth? ... NO! IT WIS IN AMON' THE BEEF!'

'Wis't a gweed duff? ... THE BEST DUFF IN SCOT-LAN'!'

The hale toon wis oot, so Ora an' Sheetlin took the wanderer home!

In the morning, Pun's guest breakfasted on a borrowed egg.

'Far's Pun?' says he.

'Oh!' says Mrs Pun, 'He's awa oot wi' the gun, I think!'

'I wis aafa sair vindicatit fin I hard 'im roarin' like yon, the streen!' says the Portsoy mannie. 'Richt sair vindicatit!'

When the guest had departed, the aalest quinie says till 'er mither, 'Fit dis vindicatit mean, Ma?'

'I think it's the Portsoy word for "black affrontit", my quine!'

The Detector

In the early days of exploration for oil in the North Sea, a great deal of time and money went into the accurate plotting of suitable positions for the siting of oil-rigs. Since the drilling of a bore-hole in the sea-bed is a highly expensive business, guess-work had to be completely ruled out. You see, it costs exactly the same to drill a successful hole as it does to draw a blank.

Thus the first arrivals on the scene were the seismic ships with their great, monstrous reels of electric cable at the stern. These cables, at least a mile in length and sometimes much longer, were towed astern of the ship day after day, and only when the ship was about to enter harbour were the cables wound back onto the reels. From the cables, powerful electric pulses 'pinged' the ocean floor, the returning echoes being recorded on highly sophisticated instruments on the ship. Besides recording the depth of water and the nature of the sea-bed (hard or soft bottom), the same instruments could chart the various underlying strata of the earth's crust, and this was what the oil-men wanted. Different echoes for different layers of rock, or sand, or chalk, or whatever, supplying information vital to the entire North Sea Oil project.

I fully realise that I have almost certainly over simplified the operation, but you're not looking for a scientific treatise, are you? Not on your Nellie! Sufficient to say that the seismic exploration still goes on, with ships and equipment which have improved beyond measure.

Now, you may recall that, some fifteen years ago, there was a buzz that the earth's crust beneath the fertile Buchan fields could be rich in precious minerals. Words like 'Plutonium', or 'Platinum', to say nothing about 'Great muckle daads o' Gold', were bandied about quite freely. Rumour had it that the fairmer at Povertyknap (you must pronounce the 'k') had actually ploughed up several sizeable nuggets which his wife had taken with her, when she 'cleared oot wi' the baker's vanman!'

The actual facts were that a considerable amount of drilling was done throughout the Buchan countryside, usually in isolated spots which were not agriculturally productive.

In several such places, small diesel-driven drilling rigs were set up, to obtain samples of the underground treasures. Now, since both diesels and drills required lubricating oil, my stock in trade, it didn't take me long to suss-out the location of most of them. I didn't sell much oil, and I didn't learn very much, apart from the fact that boring holes in the ground can be very boring indeed! Nobody seemed to know anything, because all the cores were sent south by lorry for analysis and assessment. Mind you, I did meet some really interesting people.

There was, at the same time, a light, spotter-type of aeroplane making low-level daily flights over the countryside and, since the 'plane had a short length of cable trailing behind it, I assumed that it was actually 'pinging' the ground beneath for information on underground strata, just as the seismic ships did at sea.

Now, it so happened that, in the course of my wanderings, I had a chat with an elderly farmer whose placie was set high on the brow of a certain hill.

'Hey, Peter!' says he. 'Fit's iss lad deein' wi' the airy-plane? He flees aafa low, an' I'm thinkin' he'll hae my beasts scared oot o' their skins! Some folk says he's in cojunk wi' yon lads that's borin' the holes! Div ee ken onything aboot it?'

'Awyte I ken aboot it!' says I. ''At fella has naething t' dee wi' the hole borers ava! He's fae the B.B.C., an' he's lookin' for folk that hisna peyed their T.V. licence! Ye ken fine that yon great muckle detector vans could nivver win up iss roads!'

'Dam e' bit!' says he. 'Dam 'e bit! Man, ye could be richt! I niver thocht on sic a thing!'

Now, I have it from an unimpeachable source that, next morning, the Post Office in Ellon was packed solid with folk 'sair needin' a T.V. licence!'

I wonder why! Could it be that there actually is a 'bush telegraph' in operation? And, what is more to the point, couldn't somebody somewhere be more or less entitled to a backhander fae the B.B.C.?

Maybe he's feart t' spik!